ROY CHAPMAN ANDREWS.

ENDS OF THE EARTH

BY

ROY CHAPMAN ANDREWS

With 67 Illustrations

G. P. PUTNAM'S SONS

NEW YORK   LONDON

The Knickerbocker Press

1929

Republished by Tower Books, Book Tower, Detroit, 1971

ENDS OF THE EARTH

∽

Library of Congress Catalog Card Number 78-164078

To

GEORGE PALMER PUTNAM

A FELLOW EXPLORER, AN INSPIRING
PUBLISHER AND A WARM FRIEND

PREFACE

A book of this personal character certainly needs an excuse for being. I doubt if I should ever have thought of doing it, or had the temerity to present it to the public, had it not been for a luncheon at the New York Yacht Club in December, 1928. George Putnam, Commander Fitzhugh Green and I were sitting at the table with coffee before us. In the comfortable feeling of an excellent luncheon (at Fitz's expense) I began to "reminisce" about my early days in the American Museum, of whaling cruises, and life in Conrad's country of the Malay Seas. I think I told the story of a time when I played Robinson Crusoe on an uninhabited island. George sat there with that queer light in his eyes which I have learned to fear because I know that inevitably it means a book or something else that I have no time to do.

I began to shift uneasily and suggest that it was time to go. George lit a fresh cigarette, settled determinedly into his chair and I knew that the worst

PREFACE

*had happened. It was an hour before we left and I
was committed body and soul to produce this book
before I started for the Gobi desert in the summer of
1929. It has been written on trains and ships, a part
of it even in an aëroplane. Chapters have been
mailed from cities on the west coast, from Honolulu,
Yokohama, and Peking. I never have read it in its
entirety. The responsibility for its publication I
place entirely upon the broad shoulders of the friend
to whom it is dedicated.*

Roy Chapman Andrews

Peking, China
May 5, 1929

ILLUSTRATIONS

*All photographs are reproduced from the author's collection at
the American Museum of Natural History*

vii

ILLUSTRATIONS

ILLUSTRATIONS

ILLUSTRATIONS

ENDS OF THE EARTH

ENDS OF THE EARTH

CHAPTER I

ALMOST every day someone asks me: "How did you start exploring and digging up dinosaur eggs in the Gobi Desert?"

I can answer simply enough: "I couldn't help it. I happen to have been born to do it. I am sure that I would have been a rotten failure doing anything else."

Ever since I remember I always intended to be a naturalist and explorer. Nothing else ever had a place in my mind. My first shotgun was given to me when I was nine years old. My mother was terrified at the thought, but very wisely my father said: "We can't keep him away from guns. He will get one somewhere and keep it hidden. It will be much less dangerous if I buy him one and teach him how to use it." Father was right. Nothing could have kept me away from firearms and he

3

taught me their danger and use in the best possible way. If he ever saw me point a gun, even a wooden one, at a person or handle it carelessly, it was taken away for a day or more.

I lived in Beloit, a southern Wisconsin town. Every moment that I could steal from school was spent in the woods along the banks of Rock River or on the water itself. Sundays I was not allowed to take my gun, so field glasses and notebook were substituted. I kept a record of bird migrations and knew every species of bird and animal of the region; also much first-hand information as to their habits.

Taxidermy was a necessity, so I taught myself from books. The first bird-skin I ever "made up" is now in the American Museum of Natural History with the rest of my collections. Mounting birds and mammals came to be very important to me, for I was the only one who "practiced the art" in that vicinity. I reaped a harvest during the shooting season and made all the money that I needed.

After preparatory school I entered Beloit College. During the junior year came the first tragedy of my life and the first real adventure. I was duck shooting with one of the young instructors of the college, Montague White, when the canoe we were in upset in the swollen river. White was carried by the current directly to the shore, but drowned from cramp in the ice-cold water when almost safe. I was swept out into the middle of the river. There did not seem to be a chance but I fought the deadly numbness of freezing limbs until I reached some half submerged willow trees. There was still a quarter of a mile of brown water between me and dry land. Some way, I reached it; I never quite knew how. But that hour in the icy water nearly did for me.

The next year, in June of 1906, I graduated from college and a month later came to New York. I had thirty dollars but no job. My father would have given me money but I had a boyish superstition about taking any. The thirty dollars I had made myself, stuffing deer heads and birds. I thought it would bring me luck, for to enter the American Museum of Natural History was my life ambition.

Doctor H. C. Bumpus was then director of the Museum. He said that he had no job for me. "You have to have someone to scrub the floors, don't you?" I asked.

"Of course," said he, "but a man with a college education doesn't want to begin his career scrubbing floors."

"No," I said, "I don't want to wash just any

floors, but the Museum floors are different." Mentally I pictured the floors that had been walked on by my scientific gods. I would wash those floors and love it.

And scrub them I did. Dr. Bumpus took me at my word and put me in the taxidermy department with the rising young animal sculptor, James L. Clark. Part of my work was to keep the floor clean; the rest of the time I mixed clay for modeling, helped prepare animal- and bird-skins for mounting and did any odd job. Never before or since have I been as happy.

The day I was introduced to Frank Chapman I nearly suffocated with delight. He had written my bible, the "Handbook of North American Birds." I used to hang about the meteorites in the foyer at one o'clock to get a sight of Professor Osborn when he went to luncheon. I never hoped to really meet him.

Director Bumpus did not forget me down there in the taxidermy department. He would send for me frequently to write special labels or to do some other bit of work for him. He used to inspect my floor now and then to see if the college diploma had got in the way of the mop.

A few months after I entered the Museum,

my chance came. Dr. Bumpus called me to his office and introduced me to a gray-haired gentleman who, he said, was to build a life-sized model of a whale out of paper. It was to hang in the gallery-well of the third floor, and I was to be the gentleman's understudy. I was considerably frightened but tried not to show it. My acquaintance with whales was less than nothing. You don't often meet a whale during your evening walk out in the woods of Wisconsin!

From the director's office I dashed to the Museum's library and got every book I could find on whales. Most of them discussed in learned terms the skeletons of whales, but we were to build a model. I soon found that very little had been published on the external anatomy of whales and almost nothing about their habits.

But my lack of knowledge made little difference for we were actually only to enlarge a scale model of a sulphur-bottom whale, which was to be made by James L. Clark under the immediate supervision of Dr. F. A. Lucas, then director of the Brooklyn Museum. Dr. Lucas had been to Newfoundland, where he had cut up whales and knew every inch of them from flukes to blow-hole.

The huge model became a long job. The skeleton of angle-iron and wood grew apace but the paper covering did not work. It just couldn't be kept from buckling and sinking in between the ribs. Our whale looked perfectly awful. It seemed to be in the last stages of starvation. I used to dream about it at night, and the director was in despair.

Finally he called Jimmie Clark and me to his office. "This whale is getting on my nerves," said he, "it is beyond all endurance. What shall we do?"

Jimme and I knew exactly what to do, for we were living together then and had spent many hours discussing that emaciated whale.

"Fire the paper gentleman," we chorused, "and let us finish it with wire netting and *papier-maché*."

The director beamed "Done. If you turn that wreck of a cetacean into a fat respectable whale, I'll give you both a knighthood."

Jimmie and I hopped to it with a crew of twelve men. It was amazing what a well regulated diet of wire screen and *papier-maché* did for that whale. He lost the pitiful starved appearance, his sides filled out and became as smooth as a rubber boot; we could almost feel him roll and blow as we built him up with our new tonic.

Jimmie Clark is now Assistant Director of the Museum, in charge of preparation, and I am a wanderer on the face of the earth; but our old whale still hangs in the gallery-well where he may be seen by one and all. For twenty-two years he has hung there and the inspectors report him to be in the best of health. God help those below if he ever falls for he is seventy-six feet long and weighs several tons!

He is a good whale, too. I know, because during the next few years I was destined to see many hundreds of whales. One might say that I had a speaking acquaintance with some for I studied them at sea with field glasses and camera, while they played and ate and slept. It was almost indecent the way I spied upon their private lives. And on shore, at the stations, I investigated them both inside and out as they were hauled from the water to be carved up. I even went so far as to crawl into the tummies of several just to see what sort of apartments Jonah had rented. After all that, I can still be proud of our *papier-maché* whale in the American Museum.

Building that whale marked an episode in my life. For one thing it graduated me from floor-scrubbing; for another, it set me to thinking very definitely about whales. Then fate dealt me a second ace. A real honest-to-goodness whale was killed just off the Long Island coast at Amagansett.

For many years Captain Josh Edwards, a fine old retired whaling captain, had lived there with his sons. Although seventy-six years old he could not quite give up the sea. The village kept a fully-rigged whaleboat in a shack on the beach. Sometimes the· fishermen discovered a whale cruising along the shore. At the long drawn cry of "There she blows" gallant old Captain Josh took his place in the bow of the boat and hurled the harpoon that made them fast. It was his arm, still strong under the weight of years, that thrust the lance into the Leviathan's heart.

All this happened just as it had happened half a dozen times before, only with one important difference. I was at the American Museum and the director wanted the whale. He wanted everything; photographs, measurements, skeleton, baleen, all there was that could be used for scientific study or exhibition. The morning papers told of the capture and two hours later Jimmie Clark and I were on the way to Amagansett. We were picked, naturally, for were we not even then building a whale? The director's instructions, as we dashed into and out of his office were, "Get the whole thing—every bone."

We did not learn until afterward that he never believed we could do just that. He and Dr. Lucas knew a lot about beached whales and how quickly the great bones sink into the sand. He thought we might get most of the skeleton but we never would have lost our jobs if some of the bones had been missing.

I was the most excited and the proudest boy in all New York state as we journeyed toward Amagansett. Only seven months in the Museum and off on an expedition. True, it was not an expedition to the arctic or the tropics, but it was an expedition none the less.

Arrived at the village the business of buying the whale was quickly ended. The baleen or "whalebone" was the valuable part, for at that time it was still being used for corsets and carriage whips. I believe it cost us thirty-two hundred dollars, which was only a little more than the commercial value. They threw in the skeleton but we were obligated to get the bones ourselves. The captors took the blubber which they tried out for oil.

The carcass was beached just at the edge of low tide. We knew it was a North Atlantic Right whale but the creature was so huge and so curious that at first we could hardly distinguish the head from the tail (the "flukes" had been cut off before we arrived). Finally, with the aid of the illustrations in our books, we discovered that the animal lay on its back and left side. The baleen or whalebone interested me most of all. It hung in parallel plates on either side of the mouth and was frayed out on the inner edges to form a thick mat of bristles. This mat acted as a sieve to strain from the water the tiny crustaceans upon which the beast fed.

After the fishermen had stripped off the fat, or blubber, which lies between the skin and the flesh and acts as a blanket to keep the animal warm, they went away. Jimmie and I were faced with a real problem for the skeleton lay embedded in some fifty tons of flesh. Of course we could do nothing alone and the fishermen were not at all keen to work even for high wages. The thermometer stood at twenty above zero and the wind was bitter. Finally we did persuade half a dozen men to hack away at the carcass with great knives. A horse helped to drag off huge chunks of meat by means of ropes and hooks. It was a slow business but finally the head was separated and on the beach, also the ribs of the upper side. Then the worst happened. A storm blew up from the east beating upon the exposed coast with hurricane force. We saw it coming and anchored our whale as best we could, working waist deep in the icy water. For three days the shore was a

smother of white surf. Anxiously we waited. Only
half the skeleton was on the beach and that would be
well-nigh worthless if the remainder were lost. The
fourth day was dead calm but very cold; twelve
degrees above zero at noon. When we got to the
beach a smooth expanse of sand, innocent of whale,
met our eyes. The bones had disappeared. Jimmie
and I were frantic but the anchor ropes extended
down into the sand where the bones had been. A
little shoveling exposed the skeleton, deeply buried.
It would have been difficult enough in the best circumstances to uncouple the huge vertebræ and get
the ribs of the lower side, but now it was almost impossible. As soon as we dug out a shovelful of
sand to get at a bone, the depression filled with
water. We had to grope blindly with small knives,
our arms in the freezing water up to the elbows, to
disarticulate each vertebræ. None of the fishermen
would work at any price. It was too cold and they
just sat by the fire smoking. Jimmie and I carried on
alone for three days, warming our hands every few
minutes over a driftwood fire. It seemed hopeless
and I don't mind saying that I never have suffered
more in any experience of my life than I did then.
But the director had told us to get every bone and we
simply couldn't give up.

At last some of the fishermen decided to help when they saw us two kids struggling hopelessly in that icy water. I believe it was more shame than the high wages which brought them to our assistance. Anyway, half a dozen men came and we began to make real progress. At the end of a week a huge pile of bones lay well up on the beach. We checked them off one by one on a drawing from a skeleton in the Smithsonian Institution. They were all there, except that Dr. Bumpus had told us to watch particularly for the pelvic bones. The Smithsonian drawing did not show them, but we knew what they looked like. Two small bones about a foot in length which lay somewhere in the mass of flesh about the genital organs. They are the last vestiges of the hind limbs which used to exist sixty or seventy millions of years ago when the ancestors of whales traveled the land on four legs. Of course they did not look like whales in those days probably they were small shore mammals, living like the seals partly in the water and partly out of it. As they spent more and more of the time in the sea the flukes, or tail, developed as a swimming organ and the useless legs entirely disappeared. But the pelvic rudiments still persist as two slender angular rods. Nodules of bone representing the femur are also present

One of the Early Stages in Whale Mounting; the Framework
of Wood and Steel.

Intermediate Stage in Building the Whale Model.

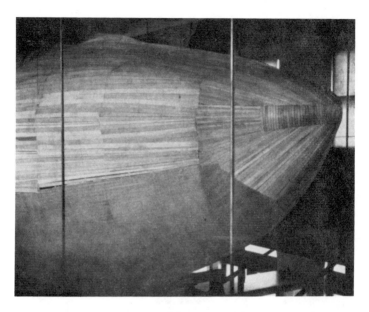

COLOSSAL FRAMEWORK FOR THE WHALE THAT HANGS IN THE AMERICAN
MUSEUM OF NATURAL HISTORY.

THE FINISHED PRODUCT! A MOUNTED WHALE IN THE AMERICAN
MUSEUM OF NATURAL HISTORY.

in some species. They are so small and so deeply embedded in flesh that they are seldom preserved in museum skeletons.

Search as we would, Jimmie and I could not find those wretched bones. They were all that remained to prevent us from doing a perfect job. Suddenly I had the idea that the flesh containing them might have been pulled off with the blubber by the fishermen who flensed the whale. We got to the try-works just in time. That particular part of the blubber had already been thrown into the huge iron caldron. With a long-handled wire net we fished about in the pot and triumphantly brought out not only the two pelvic bones but the femural rudiments still attached in their proper places.

Jimmie and I breathed several sighs of relief. Now we could go back to New York with a clean bill of bones.

The Amagansett whale was a female fifty-four feet long. She had with her a baby only a few months old, thirty-eight feet in length. The calf had left when its mother was killed and swam aimlessly along the shore toward the village of Wainscott. There it had been killed by other fishermen. The day after our arrival at Amagansett I had driven over to Wainscott and purchased the skeleton from the captors. John Nichols, new curator of fishes in the Museum, had been sent up to get the bones which he did without much difficulty. Later, it was traded to the British Museum (Natural History) for the skeleton of a dodo, that extinct bird of which you may have heard!

Cleaning up the skeleton of the whale at the American Museum was quite a job, for at that time we were not equipped as we are today to handle such huge bones. But by spring the work was done and our sulphur-bottom model had been completed. As a reward for services rendered the director let me study and describe the skeleton we had obtained. It was my first job in real science. Of course, I could read French and German and all winter I had absorbed every bit of literature regarding our species, much of which was written in those languages. Norwegian rather stumped me but I learned enough to find out what they were talking about.

By this study of the literature I was amazed to discover how little was actually known about whales. Almost everything pertained to technical description of such incomplete skeletons as had found their way into museums. Almost never had these been collected by the men who described them. Virtually nothing had been published about the life history and habits of the mamals except as whalers' accounts. It was all closet-naturalist stuff.

Here was the most extraordinary group from the standpoint of adaptation and evolutionary history in the entire animal kingdom just waiting for someone to expose its secrets. I had made up my mind long before the study of the Amagansett whale was finished that the best opportunity for a young scientist lay with whales. The men who had worked in that subject were too old. It needed youth, enthusiasm and the willingness to undergo hardships, to get out on the sea and really find out things. Moreover, the American Museum of Natural History wanted whales. It had recently been presented with a considerable sum of money by Mr. George H. Bowdoin to make such a collection. I figured that with the start which the big model and the Long Island whale had given me, I ought to get the job. It was not just "opportunism" on my part. I had become fascinated with the subject.

Our Amagansett specimen belonged to a group known as the Right Whales so called by the early Basque hunters because since they have the longest and finest whalebone and the fattest blubber they were the right kind of whales to kill.

The "wrong" whales are technically known as the Balænopteras or Rorquals, all members of which have short, coarse whalebone and thin blubber. The sulphur-bottom, a model of which we had made, is one of the wrong whales.

Then there is still another great division called the toothed whales of which the sperm is the best known representative. It also includes the dolphins and porpoises. Until comparatively recently the wrong whales or rorquals had been left severely alone by the commercial whalers. They gave too little money and by their great speed and agility wrecked too many boats. They are the grayhounds of the sea, while the right and sperm whales are slow and ponderous in their movements.

But a Norwegian by the name of Svend Foyn had invented a harpoon gun which could be fired from the deck of a small steamer. By this means the rorquals could be killed with comparative safety, towed into definite ports and there converted into oil and fertilizer at great plants. This is known as shore whaling. It first started on the coasts of Scandanavia and later extended to Newfoundland. It was there that the late Dr. Frederick W. True of the Smithsonian Institution and Dr. F. A. Lucas had made a study of certain Atlantic species. As the whales were drawn completely out of the water on to a slip by means of a steam winch, they gave opportunities such as a scientist never had had before for photographs, studies and measurements.

True had written a superb monograph on the Atlantic rorquals. However, the Pacific whales remained almost unknown. One interesting question was whether or not the large whales migrated from one ocean to another. Two shore stations had been established on the coast of Vancouver Island and one in southeastern Alaska. I made up my mind to go there.

In the meantime I had been transferred to the Department of Birds and Mammals under the wonderful pioneer naturalist, Dr. J. A. Allen. Frank M. Chapman was his associate having charge of birds, while Dr. Allen devoted himself to mammals. No sweeter character or truer scientist ever lived than Dr. Allen. The days I spent at his side were all too few, due to my restless adventurous spirit, but to work with him was one of the greatest privileges of my life. When I was admitted to this constant association with Dr. Allen and Frank Chapman, I seemed to have reached my greatest ambition.

My work consisted chiefly of revising and rearranging the study collections of small mammals.

This gave me a general and valuable perspective of mammalogy, but my thoughts were always centered upon the opportunities presented by a study of whales.

CHAPTER II

In the spring of 1908 I asked the director to be allowed to go to Vancouver Island and Alaska. I offered to go without salary if they would pay my expenses. I argued that I was an unknown quantity and that if the Museum was willing to risk a thousand dollars in expenses I certainly could risk less than half that amount in the salary I would have received. Dr. Bumpus said, "Yes," and I started off early in June on my first real expedition. I had been in the Museum less than two years then and every day of it had been filled with excitement and *joie de vive*.

Already I had found life to be a wonderful adventure. Why? Because I was doing exactly what I wanted to do, what I had dreamed of doing since I was old enough to dream of anything. Right here I want to say just one word to parents who have a growing boy. Find out, if you can, what he wants to do and when you have learned, for God's sake, and his, let him do it. Don't make him do what you would like him to do. It is his life and he must live it. The chances are he will make a success if he has a real ambition and you let him follow it. I know a hundred men who have muddled along discontented and sometimes deeply unhappy because blind parents had forced them into business when they wanted intensely to do something else. My moral may seem to be a bromide but, by Jove, the practice goes on even in this enlightened twentieth century. I know because I have such a tale of woe brought to me almost every week.

Victoria was my first objective. I had to sell myself and my plan to the whaling company. They said "All right," and put me aboard a coastal steamer bound for the whaling station in Barclay Sound on the west coast of Vancouver Island.

We had a rough passage. Great Scott, wasn't I sea-sick! It dampened my spirits but did not cool my enthusiasm even though sea-sickness became my curse. I am all over it now and no storm ever bothers me, but during all the years I spent on whaling ships I had to fight sea-sickness. Even the smell of a ship made me ill. I just had to go into it doggedly knowing full well what was coming to me. I

24

MODERN HARPOON GUN.

THE HARPOON STRIKES.

wonder if I would have the courage to face the same thing now! Honestly, I would rather stand up to a band of Chinese brigands with the numbers thirty to one against me than go through again some of those days of suffering at sea.

The whaling station was a group of large buildings at the end of a beautiful bay backed by a sheer wall of sombre spruce forest. From the water it looked like what it was—a factory. Over all hung the peculiar acrid odor of the meat dryer and whale oil. At first it nearly made me ill. Soon I came to like it. Even now when I smell something resembling it my pulses quicken with a rush of happy memories.

On shore I had to sell myself all over again to the station manager and the fifty men. There were six nationalities represented: Norwegian, American, Newfoundlanders, Japanese, Chinese and Siwash Indians. The idea of having a "professor" among them wasn't popular. They all called me "professor" for several weeks, till I got them to switch over to my first name which is short. Lord, how I hated it. Perhaps that is why any one today can get immediate action by applying that honorable title to me. I'm not a professor because I've never taught anything—at least not in a school or college.

The first whale was brought in shortly after my arrival at the station. It was a humpback, so named because it humps itself when it dives. It is one of the rorquals and two other species of the group were being taken off this coast. They were finbacks and my old friend, the sulphur-bottom, he of the whale-model I had built in the Museum.

Black as tar, splashed and blotched with white and festooned with barnacles, huge side fins or flippers fifteen feet long; enormous crenulated flukes and a flat head all covered with knobs. He made me think then, and he does now, that nature made him, found him too ugly to exist, and so tried a last moment scheme of decoration.

I got my initiation into the whaling fraternity that first day. Of course I didn't know it, but the whole station crew from the manager down to the last Chinese and Siwash were all set to watch. When one of the rorquals is killed it is at once inflated by the ship's air pumps so that it will float easily. The right whales and sperms float by themselves for their blubber is very fat but the others sink and are difficult to handle.

By the time a dead whale is brought to the station the air that has been pumped into the carcass together with the natural gases of decomposition inflate it as tight as a balloon. It will pop at the first knife thrust. When all was set for my initiating performance, one of the cutters called me over to the side of the whale. As I bent down to examine a spot he had pointed out, he thrust a huge knife into the belly. Out shot a stream of blood, almost black, and a horrible odor. Both struck me fair in the face. I went over on my back, slid down the slip and into the water. All six nationalities screamed with delight in its own particular national way; the station whistles blew and the bells rang.

It didn't take me long to realize that I was the goat. I grinned through the blood, washed a little of it off and went up to the station house to change into dry things. Evidently the initiation was satisfactory to those concerned and they figured the "professor" had passed for I never had more accommodating men to work with from that time on.

You just have to be on good terms with the station men if you want to get anywhere in studying whales. You can do nothing alone; everything is too big and heavy. Each flipper of a humpback weighs nearly a ton; the heart a thousand pounds; the stomach several hundred and so on. You cannot ever measure the beast alone. I was armed with prepared lists, having all the important measurements to be obtained but I had to step lively to get what I wanted before the carcass disappeared.

While it is being drawn out of the water the flensers attack it with their huge knives like a swarm of flies, cutting through the blubber in parallel lines the entire length of the whale. To each strip a great hook at the end of a wire cable is fastened. Then the steam winch is started and the blubber is pulled off exactly as you would peel an orange. In fifteen minutes one side is laid bare and the carcass is turned over. The other side is stripped and only the flesh and bones remain. With the aid of the steam winch the carcass is literally torn apart and in less than two hours the whole whale is being boiled for oil and fertilizer.

Blubber is a familiar term but perhaps not everyone understands the function it performs. Whales are warm-blooded as are all mammals. They must be kept warm in the cold sea water. The blubber does just that; it acts as a blanket, a non-conductor to prevent the animal heat from being absorbed by the water. We wear clothes to prevent our body-heat from escaping into the air. Whales, seals and all water mammals have blubber for the same purpose. It is merely a thick layer of fat which lies between the skin and the flesh. Fish are cold-blooded creatures and the temperature of the body changes with the medium in which they live; they do not need blubber to keep them warm.

The blubber is tough and fibrous. As it is peeled off from the whale a man follows on the carcass directly behind the great blanket-piece cutting it away from the flesh as the winch rolls it up. It is a dangerous job. If the hook gives way the blubber flies back with terrific force. I have seen a dozen accidents. Shortly after my arrival at the station a strip of blubber tore out, drove the flenser's knife into himself and nearly cut him in half. Some years later in Japan the posterior part of a whale's body which was being hauled up by the winch fell squarely upon a man. He could hardly be recognized as a human being when we took him out. I was standing near him and only escaped a similar fate by leaping off the dock into twenty feet of water as the carcass crashed upon us. I lost a four hundred dollar Graflex camera by the jump; still I would not have needed it in the next world if I had hesitated just the fraction of a second!

During my third day at the station a female humpback fifty feet long with a nursing calf was brought in. The baby was twenty-eight feet in length and only a few months old. The whalers did not want to kill the calf, they said, but it would not leave the dead mother and they were afraid it would starve to death. The milk was white and looked like cow's milk. I tested it but it had already soured and was permeated by the gases of decomposition. Later at sea I milked a whale which had just been killed and found the milk not bad, but a bit too strong to be really pleasant. Several whalemen told me that they often had fresh whale milk served on the table, but I noticed that a good excuse always was forthcoming when I suggested that they prove up on the story.

I never could be sure as to just how whales nurse their young, even though I spent many days at sea hoping to get a glimpse of the performance. There are two teats each about two inches long concealed in slits on either side of the genital opening, and these can be protruded. But a baby whale's snout is long and pointed, and the lips are six or eight inches thick. The calf must take the teat in the corner of its mouth while the mother ejects the fluid lying on her back with her belly out of the water; otherwise the baby would get more salt water than milk.

While we are on the subject of young whales it might be interesting to tell what I discovered about the size of these water-babies at birth. I once took a twenty-five foot calf which weighed about eight tons out of a sulphur-bottom whale eighty feet long. The baby was just ready for birth and the baleen was three inches in length. A sperm whale that we killed off the Japan coast some years later had done even better. She was only thirty-two feet long but her calf was fourteen feet eight inches in length —almost half the size of the mother.

One day in Alaska I noticed that a sixty-five foot finback whale which had just been brought to the station was in an "interesting condition." Everything pointed to the fact that the happy event was about to occur when the harpoon killed her. I thought something was bound to happen as she was drawn out upon the slip. It did. I found myself in attendance at the birth of a twenty-two foot baby, which, of course, was dead. No doctor of my acquaintance ever has been called upon to officiate at such an *accouchement!*

A single baby of that size would appear to be a pretty good effort, but I found six or eight instances of twins. The little fellows were lying head to tail, and I have often wondered what would happen when the birth took place. I should think that a tail presentation would be pretty difficult to manage even for a whale!

There is no definite breeding season for humpback whales. I found that out by keeping a careful record of the pregnant females, the size of each fœtus and the months in which they occurred. Spring apparently does affect their love-making somewhat but embryos were present during the winter almost as frequently. Yet in another large species, the California gray whale, mating appears to take place usually during December or early January. The period of gestation is about one year and calves are not born oftener than once in two years.

So little was known about the breeding habits of whales that I made it a special study. Most naturalists had assumed that whales acted as do land mammals. But they were dead wrong. I was once consulted by a government which was about to enact laws to protect whales. None were to be taken during the breeding season. Would I please tell them when the breeding season was? Their interest in my huge pets touched me deeply but my records of pregnant females proved that they couldn't impose blue laws or birth control on a bull whale. By the same token if they put a ban on the human hunters they would do no good by it.

I heartily agreed that whales ought to be protected but that was not the way to do it.

DISCHARGING THE HARPOON GUN.

Towing a Dead Monster to the Whaling Station.

The reason that whales are so big and that the young are of such enormous size at birth is because the animals live in a supporting medium. The female does not have to bear the weight of the baby; that is done by the water. If a land mammal grows too large it cannot move about and obtain food. A bird is limited to the weight of body which its wings can bear up in the air. A whale has virtually no limitations. It can grow as huge as it likes and that is just what it has been doing. Instead of getting smaller as the ages rolled by, whales became larger. It is rather comforting to think that we have the biggest animal that ever existed actually with us today. Even the greatest dinosaur never approximated the vast bulk of a sulphur-bottom whale. The record specimen that has ever been actually measured was 108 feet in length. It would weigh about eighty tons. A seventy-eight foot sulphur-bottom whale which Dr. F. A. Lucas weighed in sections at Newfoundland tipped the scales as follows: Total weight, 63 tons; flesh alone, 40 tons; blubber, 8 tons; blood, viscera and baleen, 7 tons; bones, 8 tons.

Because whales are so big it used to be thought that they grew very slowly and must live to a great age. That they grow slowly is not true. On the contrary the growth is amazingly rapid up to the time when they are sexually mature. In all of the large species which I was able to study, the calves more than double their length at birth during the first year. They continue nursing for at least twelve months. At the age of four or five they are able to bear young.

It is easy enough to determine whether or not a whale is old by the condition of the bones. But whether it is twenty years or two hundred is another matter. It will be pretty difficult ever to decide how long whales can live.

A bull sperm whale which was killed at one of the Vancouver Island stations while I was there showed every evidence of great age. He must have been an old warrior for he bore the scars of battles with killers, the tigers of the sea, and great scratches from the tentacles of giant squid and octopus. He even contained a little ambergris, which showed that he was not in good health at the moment. Ambergris is never found in healthy whales. It is a secretion produced in the intestines of only the sperm whale. Presumably the beaks of squid, upon which the beasts feed, cause irritations in the intestines. Ambergris is found about these spots. Sometimes it passes off with the excreta; at others it forms so rapidly that the intestinal tract is clogged and the whale dies. Then he becomes a veritable gold mine to the men who find him and have the strength of character to burrow into the mass of decomposed intestines. I can assure you that it takes a person with a strong stomach to carry out such investigations for the odor is perfectly terrible. Still, ambergris used to be worth twenty dollars an ounce and hundreds of pounds might be found in a single whale if he had been sufficiently ill. It is used as a base for the most delicate perfume! Can you beat that? Not as an odor itself, for it has only a slight and not disagreeable smell, but as a fixitive, to make the perfume last.

Incredible tales are told of the fortunes made by whalers who have found a floating mass of ambergris or a dead whale. They are like the stories of buried treasure and some of them are true. In the days when I was specializing in whales I had dozens of people bring what they hoped was ambergris to my office in the American Museum of Natural History. But in every case I had to give a negative verdict. None of them ever had real ambergris, which for hundreds of years has been one of the rarest and most valuable of animal products.

CHAPTER III

ALTHOUGH I was keen to find out everything about the inside and outside of whales, to study their habits was what I most wanted to do. That meant days of life on the little whaling vessels. Incidentally, it also meant fighting sea-sickness. I am not a bit ashamed for I have seen old sailors completely defeated after two hours on one of those dancing corks. Thank God, I never get ill any more, but I have great sympathy for those who do. The hunting vessels are somewhat larger now but at that time they were only ninety feet long. Each one had a motion all its own.

After a day or two I would become so weak that the only way I could stand up was to wrap myself around one of the stays which ran down to the deck just behind the gun platform. But I did stick at it; it is one of the few things for which I give myself full marks.

The gun is the most interesting part of a shore whaler. It is a short cannon, four feet long, with a three-inch bore, and turns easily upon a swivel up and down and from side to side. The six-foot harpoon has a double shaft, at the end of which are four twelve-inch barbs. The harpoon is tipped with a hollow point called the "bomb," which is filled with powder. This is ignited by a time fuse set for the desired interval. Three or four seconds after the gun is fired the bomb bursts, frequently killing the whale almost instantly. A large ring slides easily along the double shaft of the harpoon and to this one end of a five-inch rope is fastened. Forty or fifty fathoms of a somewhat smaller line called the "forerunner" are coiled on a heavy iron pan just under the gun, giving slack to the harpoon as it flies through the air.

From the pan the rope passes backward over a roller in the bow of the ship to a double winch and down into the hold of the ship. By means of the winch the whale is "played" as one would use a reel on a fishing rod. Usually about a mile of rope is carried and often it is not enough. I remember a big sulphur-bottom whale which the harpoon struck squarely between the shoulders. The bomb did not explode, so that the animal was almost uninjured, although the barbs of the harpoon, spread out in the blubber, held us fast. The whale dashed off like a hooked salmon. The rope smoked over the winch. Relays of men, pouring water only prevented it from catching fire. Half a mile of line ran out and the captain shouted to splice on the extra rope kept for emergencies. Nearly two miles had gone before he dared to check the rush.

Then it became an all-day battle. Foot by foot the winch wound up the rope, only to lose it again on a mad dash. But even a whale can be tired out and the captain finally put the engines to full speed astern. Still we were being dragged ahead at six knots an hour. It was not until nearly dark that a small boat put out from the ship and slipped quietly up beside the whale as it lay rolling at the surface. Then the mate thrust a long slender hand lance into the heart.

While this sort of thing went on I used to stand on the deck just behind the gun with a notebook, watch and camera ready at hand. Very little happened that I did not see and record. Previously almost all the data about the habits of whales had come from the men who hunted them. It was all pretty inaccurate. The men were too busy on their particular job of killing the animal to see and remember correctly what the whale had done. But I had nothing else to do except just that. Moreover,

WHALING STATION IN VANCOUVER.

HUGE SULPHUR-BOTTOM WHALE CHAINED TO THE WHARF AT VANCOUVER.

PREPARING TO CUT UP THE HUGE HULK.

I did not trust to first impressions, for it requires a certain amount of experience to observe accurately. In the beginning it is all too new and too exciting. At least it was to me.

I never had seen a live whale. The first one that rose close to the ship gave me the thrill of my life. It seemed as though the whole floor of the ocean had been lifted up by a submarine volcano. Just as the eruption occurred the beast spouted like a steam whistle, a terrific crash from the harpoon gun nearly deafened me and a pair of great flukes rose and fell upon the water. Then, dead silence. To save my life I could not give a coherent account of what happened. If anyone had said that the whale had sat up in the water on its tail and roared, I should have agreed that it probably did. You couldn't have proved anything by me even though I had seen it all. It required three or four such experiences to put me in a mental condition whereby I could anticipate what was going to happen and record it accurately.

A whale does not rise vertically. He comes up obliquely and the great flat head shows first. Instantly he blows or spouts. The escaping air produces a loud metalic whistle which can be heard for half a mile on a still day. Then he depresses his head, the huge back slowly rounds into view and finally the tail appears. The time to fire is when the back is exposed to the maximum height. One of the captains let me shoot three whales after I had been at sea for a considerable time.

Theoretically, I knew just how to do it, but I messed it badly the first time. I could see the big fellow rising when he was still fifteen feet under water and had the sights lined on him as he burst to the surface. I knew it was too soon to fire but somehow I pressed the trigger. Of course the harpoon struck the top of his head and glanced off. Wasn't I disgusted! A whale hasn't much brain, but even so it jarred him a bit when the hundred pound harpoon propelled by three hundred drams of powder landed on his head. He rolled over and lay still. We just had time to reload the gun before he began to notice things again. Then I let him have it right under the flipper. Thus ended the first lesson. My other two whales were killed neatly and with such despatch that I was admitted into the fraternity of gunners. I remember that the initiation cost me several cases of what we are not supposed to drink in America.

But all this happened to me on calm days. Indeed they were so calm that even I was not sea-sick. To shoot a whale in a rough sea with the tiny vessel doing a Charleston on the crest of the waves and sliding down into the troughs as though she were headed for the bottom, is quite another matter. It is not pot-hunting. In fact, it is more like shooting a bird on the wing. Now you are up and now you are down and the whale isn't waiting around until you are ready. I did not shoot any whales in that kind of weather. But I know a captain by the name of Larsen who out of a hundred shots missed only six. He took them as they came, too, fair weather and foul. When there is a thousand dollars blowing right in front of him a gunner does not hesitate just because he might spoil his shooting record!

After the whale is dead a rather amusing performance takes place. First, the huge body must be hauled to the surface with the steam winch, for most of the big species, except the sperm and right whales, sink when killed. Then a spear-pointed tube, connected by a rubber hose to the ship's air pump, is thrust into the whale's tummy. The carcass is slowly inflated until it floats high on the surface like a balloon. If other whales are in sight, the men leave the dead one marked with a flag until the end of the day's hunt.

47

Most children are taught that whales are mammals, not fish, and that they breathe air, not water. Still it does not seem to penetrate deeply enough to be remembered. At least I judge so by the number of questions that used to be asked me *apropos* of those very facts. A whale could no more live under water, unless it held its breath, than could a man. Still, it can remain below the surface for a much longer time than any land mammal. During the millions of years since the whale ancestors took up a completely aquatic existence, the bodily structure of the animals has been modified to adapt them for a life in and under the water.

When a whale dives, it takes in great lungfuls of air. During the time this is held in the body it becomes heated and saturated with water vapor. When the whale rises, it blows and this air, which condenses upon striking the colder atmosphere, forms a column of steam. Exactly the same thing happens when a person breathes on a frosty morning.

Each whale has a characteristic spout. That of all the rorquals is a single column. The sulphur-bottom has a very tall, thick spout; the humpback a low, rounded cloud; the finback a thin, high column. The right whale's spout divides at the summit and the sperm shoots out a low bushy puff forward and upward. After a short time I could distinguish at a glance what species of whale we were hunting by the spout alone.

During the long period of evolution nature has made many changes in a whale's anatomy to enable it to live in the water. The ability to hold the breath for a considerable time when beneath the surface is one of them. The longest period submergence for the rorquals which I have recorded is fifty minutes. But this is extraordinary and fifteen to twenty minutes is much more usual. Such toothed whales as the sperm and bottlenose are reported to be able to stay under water for more than an hour.

To me the most fascinating thing about studying whales at sea was in trying to discover what they did way down in the depths of the ocean. I got tantalizing glimpses of their life when they were at the surface. Still, they were only glimpses and the rest of it remained a mystery. How did they communicate under water and when widely separated? It was obvious that they had some system of telegraphing their desires to each member of a school but what that system was I could not even guess. A celebrated German anatomist, Kükenthal, thinks it is done by special sense organs at the base of the

49

rudimentary hairs on the head, but this seems highly improbable to me.

Another thing which never has been explained is how the animals can descend to great depths. What about the water pressure which becomes terrific after a hundred feet or so? How can they withstand such pressure and still rapidly rise to the surface? Anyone who has read the extremely interesting series of articles by Commander Ellsberg in the *Saturday Evening Post* will remember what difficulties the divers encountered at a depth of only one hundred and fifty feet; also how they had to be slowly "deflated" as they were brought to the surface. Yet, I personally saw a sulphur-bottom whale which had been harpooned dive straight down and take out a quarter of a mile of line. He remained below for thirty-two minutes and reappeared not more than a hundred yards away. At the time we were far out at sea and there was every reason to believe that the animal had gone down to the full limit of the line. Moreover, Captain Andersen told me of a sei whale which dived so deeply when first hit by a harpoon that it smashed its snout on rocks of the ocean floor and came up with fragments deeply embedded in the blubber. Andersen was an unusually intelligent observer and I believe his statement to be perfectly accurate. Doubtless someone will find that there are physiological adaptations of the whale's anatomy which account for its ability to adjust itself to enormous water pressure.

Toward the end of the summer in 1908 I shifted my operations from Vancouver Island up the coast to southeastern Alaska. The station was located on Admirality Island in a pretty little bay called Murderer's Cove. I don't know how it got its name, and no one seemed to know who had been murdered there. I came to it in a launch from Juneau with Mr. Victor H. Street, manager of the station. The salmon had just begun to run in the rivers whence they go on their last journey up over the rapids as far as they can push; then the females lay their eggs and die. The water of the bay was beautifully phosphorescent, and as we came into it late at night, thousands of flashing streaks darted off like submarine lightning. Behind the station lay deep masses of pine and spruce forest; in front rose tier upon tier of beautiful snow-capped mountains. There were a good many bears in the forest. Only a few evenings after my arrival we were sitting in the station house when the cook dashed in. He was white as chalk. Finally he gasped out:

"I went up to the spring for water. Just as I got

there a big bear stood up on his hind legs and grunted at me. I said 'You stay right there, Mr. Bear, I'll do all the running for both of us.' "

I went out at once with my rifle and a flash light, but the bear had gone. Probably he was just as frightened as was the cook.

The Alaska station was an ideal place to study whales. Most of the hunting was done in the inland waters of Frederick Sound where there was almost no sea. I spent many days with Captain Grahame on his little ship and was supremely happy. We were hardly ever beyond sight of land and had wonderful duck shooting when the ship anchored near shore at night.

They were killing a lot of humpbacks and finbacks there but only an occasional sulphur-bottom, for the big fellows seldom came into the Sound. It was a regular playground for the "humps." They seemed to like the quiet waters particularly for love-making. Many times I watched a pair of the huge beasts lying side by side rolling about and apparently caressing each other with their great flippers. Now and then one of them would bestow a love-pat upon the other. I suppose it was gentle for a whale but it would have crushed an ox to a pulp.

Twice I witnessed the actual mating which, I

imagine few people have ever seen. An amorous humpback is an amusing sight, I can assure you. In one case the bull whale executed an extraordinary series of acrobatic performances evidently with the object of impressing the female. He was just like a peacock showing off to his lady-love. First he stood on his head with the tail and fifteen feet of body out of the water. The great flukes were waved slowly at first back and forth; then faster until the water was pounded into spray and the terrific slaps on the surface could be heard a mile away. "Lobtailing," sailors call it.

This performance ended, he slid up close to the female rolling about and stroking her with his right flipper. She lay on her side apparently greatly enjoying his caresses. Then he backed off and dived. I was much disappointed for I thought that he had left her but she remained lying quietly at the surface. She knew well enough that he would not desert her—yet. He was gone for perhaps four minutes; then, with a terrific rush, he burst from the water throwing his entire fifty-foot body straight up into the air. It was a magnificent effort and I was proud of him. He fell back in a cloud of spray rolling over and over.

The ship had been creeping along with engines

at dead slow while all this was going on. Personally I thought it was a dirty trick to disturb them but the captain had no such scruples. He knew that the whales would let us approach as close as he wished. The ship stole up to within thirty feet before the gunner sent a harpoon crashing into the bull's side. Half an hour later the female was also killed for she had refused to leave the vicinity of her dead lord.

Of course, there is no way of knowing whether or not whales have any constancy in their marital relations. But with the whole ocean to roam in, I should judge that free-love was the order of their lives. Still their great hearts do know the tender feeling of affection; at least mother-love. I have personally witnessed many instances where a female refused to leave her calf. As a matter of fact, if a ship finds such a pair the men usually shoot the calf first because they know that then they are virtually certain to get the mother.

Some whales become very clever when they are continually hunted. I have seen humpbacks that actually played tag with a ship. They seemed to know exactly how far the harpoon gun was effective—about twenty fathoms—and kept just beyond range. After an hour or two they would be-

Two Humpback Whales Diving.

THE S.S. *Albatross.*

come bored with the game, take a long dive and leave us. An old sulphur-bottom was well known to the whalers. He had a big white harpoon scar on his back which distinguished him. But, profiting by his one sad experience, he never took any chances with a ship. If he rose nearby he would go down in a deep dive and appear a mile or two away. Still he did not leave the vicinity as whales often do when they are persistently hunted.

The animals depend upon hearing to protect them from enemies more than upon any other sense. Their eyesight is not good. It would be strange if it were, for their eyes must be adapted to see both in the water and out of it. The hearing is very keen. Before the ancestral whales took up a completely aquatic existence they had external ears. Probably these were small, like those of the seals today, but they certainly were present. We know because living whales have rudiments of the muscles which formerly controlled the external ears. Nature does not let useless organs remain very long. Sooner or later they will atrophy and disappear. Thus with the whale's ear-flaps which are merely sound collectors. If a deaf man is trying hard to hear something he cups his hand behind his ear to help catch the sound. Water is such an excellent medium for transmitting sound that external collectors are quite unnecessary to a whale.

The ear openings are minute holes on the sides of the head three or four feet behind the eyes. Only the smoothest running engines may be used on a whale ship. The animals hear the propeller, of course; still if it runs steadily and quietly they do not pay much attention to it. But any sudden change of a ship's speed will frighten them.

When whales are engaged in play or feeding they may be easily approached. They seem oblivious to danger probably because they have so few enemies. They do not post sentries even when they are asleep at the surface as do many land mammals. Sharks bother them a little and doubtless dispose of a good many sick or wounded individuals, but the killer whale is their only real enemy, other than man. The killer is a tiger of the sea, terrible in strength and ferocity; afraid of neither man nor beast, it will attack anything that swims. Yet it is a member of the porpoise family and only twenty-five or thirty feet long. The mighty teeth in both its jaws can tear even a giant whale to bits. Seals, porpoises, sharks and even man himself is fair game for them.

Captain Robert F. Scott, the Antarctic explorer, tells an amazing experience with killer whales on his last expedition. The ship was moored to an ice floe and two of their Eskimo dogs were tethered near the edge. Scott called to Ponting the photographer, to get photographs of six or seven killer whales which were swimming along the edge of the floe. They seemed very excited and raised their snouts high out of the water. Suddenly the killers disappeared. The next moment they rose under the ice striking it with their backs and setting it to rocking violently. Scott says: "Luckily Ponting kept his feet and was able to fly to security. By an extraordinary chance, also, the splits had been made around and between the dogs, so that neither of them fell into the water. Then it was clear that the whales shared our astonishment, for one after another their huge hideous heads shot vertically into the air through the cracks which they had made. As they reared them to a height of six or eight feet it was possible to see their tawny head markings, their small glistening eyes, and their terrible array of teeth—by far the largest and most terrifying in the world. There cannot be a doubt that they looked up to see what had happened to Ponting and the dogs."

The strength of the animals is shown by the fact that they had split an ice floe two and one half feet in thickness by blows of their backs or heads. Killers will apparently eat anything that swims. Fish, birds, seals, walrus, whales and porpoises are all equally acceptable. Their capacity is almost unbelievable. There is a record of thirteen porpoises and fourteen seals being taken from the stomach of a twenty-one foot specimen.

I often heard the tale that killers eat the tongue out of living whales. I never believed it until I went to Korea in 1912. There we were hunting the California gray whale, a species forty-five to fifty feet in length. Killers were also hunting them and had gathered in great numbers. The gray whales were in such terror of the killers that when a herd arrived they would become absolutely paralyzed with fright. A gray whale would turn over on its back with flippers outspread and lie helpless at the surface. Coming up at full speed the killer put his nose against the whale's lips, forced its mouth open and his head inside. Tearing out great chunks of the tongue he gulped them down. Out of thirty-five gray whales which I examined seven had the tongues eaten to a greater or less extent; in one, the entire tongue had been torn away. Many of the whales had teeth marks on their lips and the ends of the fins and flukes lacerated. My friend,

Captain Melson, brought in a gray whale one day and I noticed that the tongue was almost gone. He said that he had passed a large school of killers in the morning and later had shot a gray whale fifteen miles away. Soon he saw the high dorsal fins of the killers coming full speed for the ship. They circled about, then one rushed into the dead whale which was being towed along the vessel's starboard side. It forced its head into the mouth, ate the tongue and Melson only got rid of the beast by shooting into it with his Krag rifle. The killer lashed out with its flukes, smashing the ship's rail, and disappeared.

The gray whales seem to be more persistently persecuted by the killers than any of the other large species. They live in such a state of terror that even porpoises leaping about their heads will send them into a mad panic. Sometimes the big fellows dash wildly for shore and slide in behind rocks. Often the killer will not follow for they do not like the shallow water. They patrol up and down the shore waiting until the gray whales emerge as the tide recedes. Some killers are not in the least afraid of a ship. The whalers are glad when the sea-tigers arrive. They will quickly throw a school of whales into such a panic that the men have no difficulty in getting fast.

I might give many more stories about killers but these are enough to show that they are highly dangerous fellows. Apparently they are the terror of everything that swims the sea.

All the rorquals feed almost exclusively upon a small shrimp about half an inch long. At times these float in great masses near the surface. In Frederick Sound I had a wonderful opportunity to watch the feeding operations of humpbacks and finbacks, for the water was calm and the whales would allow the ship to come up very close. With my powerful glasses I could see them as plainly as though I were a dozen yards away. A humpback would swim along with his cavernous mouth wide open, then close it suddenly. The water spurted out from between the whalebone plates leaving hundreds of pounds of shrimp on the soft flabby tongue. He would roll on his side, throw his great flipper in the air, and swallow; then begin all over again. I took six barrels of shrimp out of the stomach of a single sulphur-bottom whale at one of the Vancouver Island stations.

These whales do not eat fish if shrimp are obtainable, but sometimes they will swallow herring or sardines. Their throats are small—only six or eight inches in diameter—and they could not digest large fish even if they were able to swallow them.

CHAPTER IV

I DISCOVERED a good many more new facts about whales during the summer I spent at the Vancouver Island and Alaska stations. But I am not now supposed to be writing a book on whales; that has been done already. I went back to New York in the late autumn of 1908 and found Director Bumpus pleased with the results which had been obtained with his seven hundred dollars. It was highly successful from my standpoint because I was fairly launched in a big subject. I was still supposed to be working on the study-collection of small mammals and stuck pretty closely at it during the mornings. The afternoons were spent at Columbia University which I had entered for the degree of Doctor of Philosophy. One of my great good fortunes was to attend the last series of lectures which were given by Professor Osborn as Professor of Zoölogy in Columbia. The class in the Evolution of the Vertebrates was in charge of Professor W. K. Gregory. There were only eight or ten of us and

64

we had a glorious time. Frequently, we would become so engrossed in philosophical discussions that we would adjourn to a small restaurant for dinner and continue the arguments until far into the night.

The university work kept me busy every evening until the small hours of the morning and Sundays I always spent dissecting at the College of Physicians and Surgeons in the graduate anatomical laboratory. There was no time for play but the work was so interesting that it was the only recreation I wanted. Every day was filled with new experiences either in the Museum or the University. I was supremely happy. That winter I lectured for the first time. My whale pictures were so new and different that they made a real hit. Of course I knew nothing about lecturing and for experience entered the City Board of Education lecture list. I got experience, all right, but not much else. The fee was only ten dollars a night and I was sent to the most extraordinary places. My first assignment happened to be at the Five Points Mission way down on the East Side of New York. I knew nothing about Five Points and went there in full evening dress; white tie, white waistcoat and all the rest. I found the barn-like room half full of my audience. Few of the men had coats or collars and the women were in corresponding negligee. I felt like nothing on earth in my tail coat. There was a long delay and I asked the "chairman" why he did not begin.

"We are waiting for the police," said he, "usually there is a riot if they don't like the lecturer. They throw things at him." I felt warmer and warmer and looked around to see what "things" they were likely to heave at me. Finally three policemen arrived and I was presented to the audience. I knew something had to be done or my name probably would be tomato or cabbage. Moreover, it was my only dress suit and I did not want to have it ruined. So I began by saying that it was hot in the room and if they didn't mind I would get myself comfortable. I stripped off my coat, waistcoat, collar and tie and opened my shirt in front. This put me somewhat in harmony with the surroundings and I started in with the lecture, full steam ahead. It went all right, too. I tried to make them feel and hear the rush of the sea, the roar of the gun and the thrill of the hunt. I never worked harder for I had visions of being plastered with over-ripe eggs if their attention wandered. But they stuck it out to the bitter end. Several men and women sidled up in an embarrassed way while I was re-clothing myself and thanked me for the lecture. I felt that it was a real triumph.

66

BIG NET HUNG FROM THE SIDE OF *S.S. Albatross*.

WASHING THE NET AFTER A DEEP-SEA HAUL.

I did a good deal of lecturing that winter and came to enjoy it enormously. There was always inspiration in knowing that all those people had come to hear what I had to say; that I could tell the story to hundreds instead of giving it to only one or two. Anyone who is intensely interested in a subject likes to talk about it. I was so fascinated with my job that it seemed the biggest and most important thing in the world. I just couldn't imagine anyone not keen to know about the life story of a whale!

I picked up a good many lectures besides those assigned me by the Board of Education. One of them was at a fashionable girls' school. I arrived just in time to dress and was horrified to discover that I had forgotten my white tie. There were no men about the place. I had to think of something or go on in my street clothes. Suddenly there flashed into my mind an advertisement that I had read in the subway that very day. It was about a new kind of combination underwear for men. "What are shirt-tails good for?" it read. "By Jove, they are good for a dress tie right now," said I. There was a pair of scissors in my kit and in two minutes I had cut a lovely white tie out of my left shirt-tail. It was a bit limp but I am sure that no one suspected where it had come from.

That same winter at another girls' school I forgot my black dress shoes. My other shoes were of a peculiarly poisonous shade of yellow which was very popular at that time among college students and those newly graduated. I thought that they were beautiful but by no stretch of imagination could I see myself in full evening dress and yellow shoes. Moreover, I was pretty young and the girls of the school were about sixteen. I knew that I wouldn't have a chance. But fortunately it had been raining and I had rubbers. So I explained my predicament to the janitor who controlled the lights, put on my rubbers and sallied forth. Only about two inches of yellow showed above the rubbers. The janitor turned off the lights and I pussy-footed out on the stage. After the lecture, I sneaked off again before the lights were on and gained my room unobserved. I suppose the girls thought I was frightened of them!

In June of that spring (1909) I went on another short expedition to the St. Lawrence River. Dr. C. H. Townsend, Director of the New York Aquarium, knew of a place where white whales or porpoises were being taken in nets. These are most beautiful animals, white as driven snow, true spirits of the North. He thought it would be a splendid idea to bring back several alive for exhibition in the great central pool of the Aquarium. It was a perfectly practicable plan for the porpoises are only twelve or fifteen feet long and transportation would not be impossible if they were properly treated. My idea was to suspend them on broad strips of canvas in a narrow crate. The animals must not rest upon their sides or breasts for since they are accustomed to living in a supporting medium, the weight of their own bodies would so press in the weak ribs that the lungs could not be properly inflated and they would suffocate. My instructions were to get live porpoises if it were possible. If not to bring back skeletons, plaster casts, notes, and measurements for a life-sized model in the American Museum.

Although white porpoises are a true Arctic species and are seldom found far away from the ice, during the spring they come into the St. Lawrence River by thousands. A few even spend the summer there. They are quite valuable, for the skin furnishes the porpoise hide of commerce and the fat, particularly that about the jaws, gives a very fine watch oil. Certain French dwellers along the St. Lawrence make porpoise-hunting their business.

The place where the animals were being taken in nets was near Tadousac at the mouth of the Saguenay River. Wind and weather conditions must be just right or the porpoises will not come into the tide rips where the net can be employed. They were not right when I arrived and the men seemed to think that there was little probability of an early change. After waiting ten days I gave it up and went off with three Frenchmen on their yawl to kill some porpoises for the Museum. It was great fun for I could do the hunting myself. We sailed along comfortably until we saw porpoises feeding in the tide rips. Many times we passed the brown young ones, but I did not want them. Nothing but the old white fellows would do. At last we discovered a school industriously engaged in catching fish near the end of an island. I put off in a canoe with one of the Frenchmen to paddle. My weapon was an old ten-gauge shotgun loaded with a lead ball. Some of the whales were young and we passed them, but a big white fellow slipped under very close and headed directly for us. He came up with a sharp "putt," as he blew and dived again. The next rising would bring him hardly twenty feet away. In a few seconds the telltale patch of swirling green water began to smooth out right in front. I fired the instant his round snowy head appeared above the surface. The beautiful white animal shot into the air, falling back almost on the canoe. Dropping the gun I grabbed a small harpoon and thrust with all my strength. At the touch of the iron the ghostly form again flashed into the air but the Frenchman had tossed over the float and backed out of danger. The whale fought desperately to free itself dashing from side to side and lashing the water into foam with its flukes. Watching my chance I fired another ball into its neck. Straightening out it rolled belly up and sank.

We got four other white whales that week. I took the skeletons and gave the men the blubber and skin; also a few dollars additional so that everyone was happy. The best specimen we beached well up in a sandy cove near Tadousac where I could work without interruption in making plaster moulds. The completed cast of my white whale hangs in the new hall of Water Mammals of the American Museum. Besides the skeletons I had enough new data on the habits of the species and photographs to make an interesting scientific paper. Anyway it was interesting to me but I suppose no one except a very few zoölogists have ever read it.

I returned to New York at the end of June expecting to settle down to a summer of hard study in the Museum. But such was not to be. In a month I was off again, this time to begin my wanderings in the strange far places of the world—Borneo, Celebes and the fairy islands of the South Seas.

CHAPTER V

I RETURNED from the St. Lawrence River at the end of June 1909. A month later the Director of the Museum called me to his office.

"Would you like to go to Borneo and the Dutch East Indies?" he asked. Just like that! Would I like to go to Borneo?

"Can a duck swim?" said I. Probably I did not use exactly those words, but whatever I did say got my idea across emphatically. It was ridiculous to ask me if I wanted to go anywhere. I wanted to go *everywhere*. I would have started on a day's notice for the North Pole or the South, to the jungle or the desert. It made not the slightest difference to me. I was young, without a care or responsibility in the world and keen for the adventure of life. Already it had begun to be such an adventure as I never had dreamed of. So it has been ever since.

The Director went on to explain. "The U. S. Bureau of Fisheries have asked if I would loan you to go on a cruise of the exploring ship *Albatross*. They want to investigate the small islands of the East Indies and to do deep sea dredging. Your job will be to study the porpoises. Doubtless there are many new species to be discovered. No one has done it. Also you are to collect mammals and birds wherever possible."

It was all very plain and matter-of-fact to him, but not to me. The *Albatross* was the most famous deep sea exploring ship of her time. Mere mention of the name brought visions of strange new lands, of thrilling adventures, of Robinson Crusoe islands!

I went back to the Sigma Chi fraternity house at Columbia University where I was living, literally walking in a dream. A fortnight later the dream was translated into reality for I was actually on the way to Seattle. There I got a ship for Japan. Dozens of girls swarmed on the deck before we left. I remember how disappointed I was when all the pretty ones got off leaving only six or seven who were very hard on the eyes. They were going to a mission station in Korea.

Japan was all I hoped it would be and that is saying much. Fujiyama smiled at us above the clouds as we steamed into the sun-lit bay at Yokohama. The Japanese say that if you see Fuji when

MALAY VILLAGE.

The Noon Hour in a Sumatra Village.

you first come to Japan you will return many times. Certainly in my case it has proved true. The strange new life, the babel of a foreign tongue, the costumes and the colors thrilled me mightily. Now, much of it has vanished. Motor cars and trams replace the swarming rickshaws; European dress is driving out the graceful kimona.

Shanghai and Hongkong were equally satisfying but in a different way. Even then the heat and dust and odor did not distress me as they do most strangers. The subtle lure of the East was already in my blood.

We pitched and rolled our way across the China Sea in the tail end of a typhoon. Out there is where the typhoons hatch. When one has grown sufficiently to start life for itself, it sweeps across the water toward Hongkong, up past Formosa and Japan and out to sea. They are terrifying storms. A deluge of rain and furious wind which whirls and twists along like a tortured devil. I have weathered three; one on shore and two at sea. I don't mind telling you that three is more than enough.

Manila pleased me as much as Japan and China had done. The modern city of today was then just coming into being. The hotel was the old Metropole at the end of Santa Cruz bridge. The Army and Navy Club occupied a picturesque Spanish house in the walled city; the moat was still a slime-filled ditch.

I was to join the *Albatross* at the Cavite Navy Yard. She was south near Zamboanga, and would not return for several weeks. The late Dean C. Wooster, Secretary of the Interior for the Island government was a naturalist of repute. When he learned that I was from the American Museum of Natural History, he said "I'll do anything I can to help you."

That meant a good deal, for Wooster was the big man of the Islands. I wanted to get busy at once, and he virtually turned over to me one of the little government steamers. He told me of a small island which he had long been wanting to explore. It was off the usual track of coastal vessels. The ship could drop me there and pick me up when it returned.

A week later on a glorious tropical morning I was rowed with two Filipino boys toward the low shores of a palm clothed island. Water blue as indigo covered the outlying coral reef over which floated fishes painted in rainbow colors. We landed in a sandy cover and made a rapid reconnoissance of the island. It was uninhabited but had a spring of good water; that was the important thing. After leaving food for five days and our collecting gear, the ship steamed away. I was a Robinson Crusoe with two men Fridays.

For a week I had a glorious time exploring the island, trapping small mammals and collecting birds. At night we slept in canvas sea-hammocks swung between palm trees to keep away from ants and land crabs.

But the ship did not return at the appointed time. Neither did she come the following day, nor the next. Our food was gone and almost all my ammunition. Still we were doing well enough. There was one family of monkeys on the island—a mother and father and two babies. We ate them at the end of the first week, but I saved one in alcohol as a specimen. Monkey is not bad—if you are hungry enough! Nevertheless, you could put me in the primate house at the zoo without the slightest danger to the inmates.

When ten days had passed and no ship the Filipino boys decided that they were going to die and the sooner it was over the better. I verily believe that they would have given up and starved to death. But I had not the slightest intention of dying. As a matter-of-fact I was having a bully time for I knew that eventually Secretary Wooster would send a boat. All we had to do was to keep alive until he did. Before the last shotgun shell had killed its last bird, I made the natives get busy. Thousands of beautiful white pigeons with black wings and tails came to roost in the trees. There were plenty of fish on the reef. All we needed to get them both was a net. The boys made a net out of rattan and palm fibre. I evaporated sea water for salt and we had the necessities of life—salt, fish and birds. There was plenty to do for we could still trap small mammals. I remember thinking that I ought to have all the appropriate feelings of despair at being thus abandoned but for the life of me I could not work up anything of the sort. The ship was gone two weeks. She had had propeller trouble and the captain was terribly worried about us. When he found how comfortable and happy we had been he became equally disgusted.

Eventually the *Albatross* arrived at Cavite and I met my shipmates. She was manned by the Navy and carried about twelve officers and sixty men. Also there were three naturalists besides myself and a Japanese artist who painted fish. Almost immediately the ship left for Borneo. We stopped for a short time at the village of Tawao, British North

Borneo, and then proceeded to Sibitik Island. Here the ship waited while I went inland to shoot.

My first impression of a Borneo forest was one of sound rather than sight. Myriads of singing insects filled the air with such a medley of shrill vibrations that my ear-drums ached. I prayed for just a moment of silence. But silence did not come until after the daily deluge of rain at half-past four. There were sights enough too for it was just as I had imagined a Borneo jungle ought to be. An impenetrable wall of giant trees stretching up and up seemingly almost to the clouds. The white camphor-wood and *kayu rajah* or "king tree," more than two hundred feet tall, dominated all the rest. Each was hung with a tangled network of vines and creepers; below palms and banana trees grew thickly between the larger trunks.

I soon found that it was impossible to move in the forest except by cutting a path with a huge native knife, *machete*. I tried to break through an opening but in two minutes was caught in a dozen places. Three-inch palm thorns had me by the trousers and spiny "wait-a-bit" vines laced across my chest and back. I lost my temper and tried to back out, but I tried just once! The more I pulled the deeper went the thorns. Every move was agony. Finally, Miranda my native boy, cut me loose. My clothes were in rags and I was streaming with blood.

Miranda looked at me and grinned. "Master better learn not get angry. No use. Better use knife," said he.

He was right. The jungle is no place for an impatient man. When I got back to the ship that night my feet were sloshing in the high boots at every step. I thought it was water and was horrified to pour out pints of blood. At least a dozen leeches had worked their way through the eyelets and into the top of each boot. My legs were covered with tiny red spots from which the blood oozed in a thin stream. The wretched leech deposits a serum wherever he takes hold which prevents the blood from coagulating. The wound keeps open, is sure to become infected and then you have a nice mess. There is just one way to beat his game. Wear high shoes with the tongue sewed in and spiral woolen puttees. The leeches can't work through the wool folds if they have been properly wrapped.

I set a line of sixty traps for small mammals. The next morning every one was sprung and I had only one mouse. He was but little more than a skeleton for the ants had found him before I did. I could not imagine what had sprung the traps until I saw some huge ants, an inch in length, playing about one of them. That gave me an idea. I baited a trap, set the trigger lightly and made myself comfortable to watch. In a few moments a huge ant climbed on the pedal and began pulling at the bait. Then two others joined him. In five minutes they had sprung the trap.

Land crabs, noisome creatures which will devour a man if he is helpless, were as bad as the ants. Between these two pests, the collecting of small mammals was very poor, but with larger things I was more successful. Proboscis monkeys were fairly abundant. They are huge brown fellows with long bare finger-like snouts. It was not easy to shoot them for they could travel at full speed through the jungle, swinging from one tree to another, while I had to cut my way slowly along the ground. Finally one herd stopped to feed in a grove of bananas and I shot three before they discovered where the bullets were coming from.

Once I had what might be called a real adventure with a huge python. There are many snakes in the jungle but one seldom sees them for the cover is so thick that they can glide away unobserved. I do not believe that I actually saw more than half a dozen during as many months. The python incident would have been horribly fatal except for Miranda, my native boy. We were walking along a narrow animal trail in the jungle. I was ahead and going slowly. Slowly, I felt myself jerked violently backwards and heard Miranda's excited voice.

"Excuse Master, but big snake right there. You shoot him quick."

He pointed to a thick branch overhanging the trail. Try as I would I could see nothing except a gray tree trunk. Miranda was frantic.

"There, there, don't you see him?"

I did not. Then the breeze moved the leaves a bit and a patch of sunlight fell squarely upon a glittering eye in a dark flat head. Following it back, what I thought was a tree trunk resolved itself into the vast bulk of a python lying close along a low overhanging branch. Perhaps ten feet of the body showed behind the head; the remainder was lost in the thick shadows of the tree.

I backed thirty feet away, lined my sights on that glittering eye and fired. A cyclone seemed to have struck the jungle. I caught a glimpse of yards and yards of snake, writhing, twisting, slashing. Vines and creepers were torn, small trees shattered. Miranda and I ran, for it seemed that anything might happen. It must have been half an hour before the jungle was quiet again and we dared to slip back to where the eruption had taken place. The snake was there all right, its enormous body twisted into folds and knots. My bullet had smashed the head to pulp. We straightened it out as best we could and I paced the length. It was pretty close to twenty feet.

Without doubt Miranda's sharp eyes had saved me from a rather horrible death. The python had been lying on the low branch watching the trail. If a wild boar or deer had stepped along the path, fold after fold of the huge body would have been thrown about the beast and its life crushed out. Probably I would have met the same fate. After all, a python is no respecter of persons and anything that moves and breathes and has flesh would be grist for its mill. I could almost feel my bones being crushed as I watched the still twitching muscles knot themselves tighter in the throes of death. We were so far from the ship that it was hopeless to skin the reptile, so we left it as it lay. I did not like to do that even to a snake, for I never have killed except for food or specimens. I have shot during my entire life. It has been part of my job. Many thousands of birds and animals have fallen to my gun but for every one there was a real cause. I find no pleasure in killing just to try my skill. Now, after many years, it has become distasteful to shoot even for food. Dangerous animals are somewhat different. If you give them an even chance they can strike back.

On the way back to the beach I thought I heard an aëroplane. I was perfectly convinced of it, but nothing was visible in the sky except a great bird far above the trees. Down it sailed and I realized that this was the aëroplane. The top of a huge camphor-wood tree bent under the weight as it alighted on the thin branches. The shotgun was useless at that height but a steel bullet from my rifle brought it crashing down. It was a horn-bill—the first I had ever seen alive. After looking at the stiff quills of the wing feathers, I realized that they had made the hum I had mistaken for a distant aëroplane.

Parrots were everywhere. One island which we visited simply swarmed with them. I collected eleven different species and almost every officer and blue-jacket on the ship purchased one for a pet. The vessel became a floating aviary and the noise was nerve-racking. Most of them had been taught Malay but they learned English quickly enough. Finally a big white cockatoo belonging to one of the officers jumped down a sky-light into the captain's cabin and nearly wrecked the place. An edict was issued against all parrots. The sailors were furious but my collection of bird-skins grew correspondingly.

One day in the late afternoon we dropped anchor off a tiny, heavily forested coral island. I went in with two natives to have a look at the place. From the edge of the jungle I saw half a dozen low trees which seemed to bear strange black fruit. It hung in masses from every branch and actually was in motion. I thought I had the "hebe-jibies" and stepped up very gingerly toward the nearest tree squinting my eyes against the sun.

Bats. They were not fruit but fruit-bats. Further back in the shadows the jungle was alive with them. Thousands upon thousands hanging head downward like huge black pears. They were just beginning to awake after their day-long sleep and were quarreling and murmuring, probably discussing their dreams, or whatever bats talk about. When the breeze swept out from the depths of the jungle it brought a sweetish musty odor, almost overpowering.

At last I fired at a cluster hanging right over the beach. Both barrels, one after the other into that black squirming mass. Then there *was* a row. A pandemonium of shrill squeaks and the whole jungle seemed to belch bats. Fifty thousand, a hundred thousand, I couldn't even estimate. There might have been a million for all I knew. The sky was black with them. Each had a wing spread of more than two feet but there was a strange absence of noise. Nothing like a roar of wings such as birds would make. Just a strange swish when they went by. They fluttered up like a cloud of wind-blown leaves, drifted over the ship and disintegrated into thousands of black flapping entities. It was a weird sight; there was something ghastly and unhealthy about it that made me shiver. Like a breath of damp stale air from the blackness of a dungeon.

It is strange that bats should affect Occidentals that way. Chinese consider them to be omens of fortune. It is one of their good luck signs. You will often see it used in the decorations of rugs and embroideries. Bats and clouds! These big fellows are not like the blood-sucking vampires of South America; they feed almost entirely upon fruit. What tons they must destroy!

The strange birds and mammals gave me a wonderful time on land but with porpoises it was not so good. We saw only two or three schools and they did not seem to like us. According to theory, they ought to have played about the bows of the ship and given a continuous acrobatic performance. I have seen them do it sometimes but those we found were not properly trained. They left us severely alone and even when I went out in a small boat we never got near enough to shoot or use the harpoon. Still, I didn't mind much. There were quite enough other things to keep me busy every second.

CHAPTER VI

The ship's dredging operations were fascinating. At that time the *Albatross* was the best equipped vessel in the world for deep-sea work. Part of her program on the expedition was to take soundings for a study of the ocean bottom and to make dredge hauls to collect the fish and invertebrate life of the great depths. The men always took soundings before the dredge was let down. A forty pound shot was used for a mile or less; a sixty pound weight for greater depths. The wire also carried a mud-cup to bring up a specimen of the ocean's floor, a thermometer which automatically tripped to register the temperature at the bottom and another cup to obtain a sample of the deepest water to be tested for specific gravity. All this happened at one time when the shot reached the bottom, where it will remain "until the sea gives up its dead."

Having recorded these data for future reference the boom was swung over the side and the great dredge slowly lowered into the water. It consisted of a net twenty or twenty-five feet in length, fastened to a twelve foot steel frame. This held open the mouth of the net and acted as a runner when it was dragged over the ocean floor. When the dredge had reached the bottom the ship steamed forward at about two knots an hour. After thirty minutes, sometimes much longer, and the steam winch slowly brought the dredge to the surface. Usually it was a quarter filled with mud. Mud so cold that the men had to wear long gloves while working in it under the blazing heat of an equatorial sun! We could have a bottle cooled in a few moments by thrusting it into the soft ooze.

With a hose the men washed away much of the mud; then the bottom of the net was untied and the contents dropped into a table-trough on the deck. I was always keen to see what the dredge had brought up from the ocean depths. Often we had the strangest fish imaginable, especially adapted for life in the complete darkness of the submarine world. Fish with eyes far out on stalks; with phosphorescent spots along the sides like the glowing portholes of a ship; fish carrying little lanterns to light their way. Sometimes in the sudden ascent to the surface and release from the great pressure to which they were accustomed, they were turned almost inside out; usually those from great depths were badly damaged.

The contents of the dredge from very deep hauls —a mile or more—were disappointing, at least in variety. Sea urchins (Echinoderms) led all the rest, though star fish were abundant too, if I remember correctly. Off the coast of New Guinea the figure-head of a ship came up in the net. It was heavily encrusted with barnacles but I scraped off enough to see that it represented the bust and head of a woman. I looked at it for a long time wondering about its tragedy. Was it pirates, war or ocean-storms that had sent the vessel to the bottom. I was romantic enough to hope for pirates.

Dynamiting fish on the coral reefs was always exciting. In the wonderful water-gardens, more gorgeous than any ever seen on land, brilliant fish, yellow, green and purple, floated in and out among the waving sea-fans. With the aid of a water-glass we could discover types new to our collection. Then the beautiful gardens would be shattered by a few sticks of dynamite exploded near the surface. Perhaps half the fish would rise and float belly up but many others sank quietly among the broken coral flowers. Many were retrieved with a long-handled

Dense Vegetation on Gilolo Island, Dutch East Indies.

The Mayón Volcano.

trident and still others by natives who dived for those we could not reach.

One of the men who did the dynamiting was rather absent-minded. It doesn't pay to be absent-minded when handling dynamite. Just one accident can happen; there never is a chance for a second—at least to the same person. When exploding a surface charge this man had a habit of tying two or three sticks together, lighting the fuse and throwing the dynamite forty or fifty feet away. He was in a pram with two sailors. He lit the fuse but threw out the match and dropped the dynamite in the bottom of the boat. The order of importance had just reversed themselves while his wits were wool-gathering. His first impulse was to leap forward away from the spitting fuse but in a second he jumped back, grabbed the dynamite and threw it as far as he could. He was just in time. The charge burst in mid-air doing no damage. The men in the boat were pretty sick; in fact, they could not climb the sea-ladder when they rowed back to the ship. Then the captain issued orders that in future all dynamite was to be exploded by the electric battery.

Several times we saw with the water-glass a small brilliantly purple fish swimming about in the coral. We had had nothing like it and fired charge after charge but never got the little fellow we were after. Finally a native caught one alive. The chief naturalist saw that it closely resembled a small yellow-white fish of which he had a dozen specimens. That gave him the idea that there might be a sudden change of color with death. He killed the little captive and sure enough the brilliant color faded like the afterglow of sunset.

The first town we visited in the East Indies was Menado in the northern tip of Celebes. All of us were enchanted. It was like a village from a picture-book; a place for exhibition, not to live in. Great wide streets lined with magnificent trees and feather-leafed palms, perfect little houses, velvet lawns and gorgeous beds of flowers. Roads which seemed to have been newly swept. Natives in brilliant sarongs and scarlet fez. Everything scrupulously neat and clean; "spotless town" if there ever was one. It was a fair sample of all such places in the East Indies; at least all that I saw. A wonderful spot to retire for one's old age in which to live out the twilight of life and die in a paradise of trees and flowers.

But not a place in which to work. Oh, no, not that! I did not see any white men working. I think they do go to their offices, if such things exist, for

a short time in the very early morning. But when
the sun is high they retire to the coolness of shaded
verandahs and darkened bed-rooms there to sleep
away the hours of heat. The streets are deserted
save for the brown-skinned natives. About five
o'clock in the afternoon the white population be-
stirs itself. Women (mostly extremely fat) in
filmy dresses and men in white duck clothes gather
at the Club or drive about the streets until the soft
darkness of the tropic night drops like a stage cur-
tain, shutting out the palms and flowers. But it
does not send them off to bed. The night is the
time in which to live; the day for sleep. Truly a
lotus-eater's existence.

Were it not for the ubiquitous Chinese merchant
precious little business would be done in these toy
cities. But he is everywhere with his bland smile
and ceaseless industry, ever ready to accumulate the
odd guilder of which the Malay is too indolent to
think. Many of them have become fabulously rich
in rubber and other ventures. It was rumored that
fortunes had been made in opium, but I saw no
smoking. The ordinary Malay prefers the more
harmless but disgusting *betel* nut. Wrapped in a
bit of green leaf with a pinch of lime, the nut is
chewed by man, woman and child. Some of the

girls were exceedingly pretty but the red-stained lips marred their beauty.

We spent only a few hours in Menado and then were off to a tiny coral island in the great gulf. I landed and shot a score of birds, all new to my collection. That night I sat in the laboratory until long after midnight skinning out the specimens. But it was wasted effort, all because of a goat! That wretched beast was the ship's mascot. It had been on the *Albatross* for nine years—three full cruises. At the end of each three years it was solemnly mustered out, given a huge feed of cigarette papers, which were its especial delight, and then signed on for another cruise. A stiff white collar about the neck and a green tie were its uniform on such important occasions. The animal had the run of the entire ship. Even the captain's cabin and the officers' wardroom were not inviolate. It was bad form to be annoyed even when one found one's shoes partially eaten or a shirt minus a sleeve. Nothing was safe. The brute could tread as softly as a cat on occasion and that was always when it was up to some particularly devilish trick.

That night that I was laboring over my birds in the laboratory, as each one was skinned I tossed it behind me into a box. At last they were done and, half asleep, I prepared to cover them lightly with wet sand for safe-keeping until morning. To my amazement the box was empty. Even the last bird I had skinned was gone. On deck I heard just the faintest sound and dashed out in time to see the goat disappearing toward the forecastle. He had devoured them all and even though they were well dusted with arsenic the beast was not even ill!

The little island of Ternate not far from the coast of New Guinea was an interesting stop. I climbed the sub-active volcano, a beautiful regular cone, 5600 feet above sea-level. On the way up I felt as though I was going through a grocer's shop for the lower slopes of the mountain are covered with pepper, nutmeg, clove and cocoa trees. Long before reaching the summit I could hear the roaring of steam from the crater over which hung a beautiful white cloud shot through with yellow streaks. I had a good look into the giant pit and then went down.

The captain was much exercised when he found that I had been to the top for the officials had warned him not to let anyone go to the crater. Often the shifting winds suddenly swirl the sulphur cloud about the summit. If a man happened to be there he would be instantly suffocated. But I had

had luck, as usual. "Fools rush in where angels fear to tread!"

Everyone was madly buying paradise birds at Ternate. Each officer and sailor had some sweetheart in some port who would extend special favors for such a gift. The price rose alarmingly upon our arrival, but still the finest birds could be had for less than five dollars. At that time in America they were worth forty or fifty dollars.

Not long after leaving Ternate one of the sailors appeared on deck roaring drunk. He was promptly put in the brig until he sobered up but a few days after his release it happened again. The same performance was repeated frequently during the next month. All efforts of the officers to discover where he got the stuff were unavailing. The other bluejackets swore solemnly that they did not know, and the captain became convinced that they were telling the truth.

Finally men were detailed to watch the inebriate night and day. For a long time he eluded his chaperons but at last they caught him. Can you imagine what he had been doing? Stealing into the laboratory during the night and drinking the alcohol out of a huge jar filled with snakes and lizards!

At Buru we met with the first unfriendliness

from natives. It is a large heavily forested island only partially explored. Two of us went ashore and penetrated far inland. We found three or four Malay villages but all had been deserted hurriedly. Fires were left smoking and food half eaten. Not a native could we see. Still, we had the uncomfortable feeling that eyes were always peering at us from the blackness of the jungle. I was sure of it. My nerves were on edge and I tried every trick of woodcraft which I knew to catch our pursuers but in vain. Only once or twice I saw a bush sway unnaturally or found freshly cut vines or twigs. We expected to feel an arrow or a spear in the back every moment. Nothing happened and we pushed on while those unseen phantom figures hovered on our flanks.

I liked it less and less. We knew enough about Malay habits to be very careful on the way back. The trail produced just what we had expected. Poisoned bamboo stakes with needle-sharp points, cleverly concealed in the undergrowth of the path. They were at exactly the right height and angle to catch us in the thighs. One deep gash would have doomed a man to pushing clouds for all eternity. The natives often get deer and pigs that way.

Abruptly quitting the trail we cut through the

jungle to a stream some distance on the left and worked down it in the water. Never were we without that devilish, creepy feeling of being watched by unseen eyes until we reached the safety of the open beach.

Christmas was spent at Macassar in the Celebes. I don't think I will ever forget that day or the "head" I had next morning. Word was sent to the Club that we would keep open ship for all the foreign residents. Cocktails were served in the wardroom and there was real ice. The hospitable Dutchmen had had neither ice nor cocktails for many moons and they came in droves all through the day. For the honor of the ship someone had to be there to entertain each new group. The Executive Officer arranged us in shifts but few of us lasted till dark. Afterward, we always referred to it as the "Battle of Macassar."

The governor invited the captain, doctor and myself to a crocodile shoot next day. I did not get any crocodiles. I couldn't hit them! Not after the previous day's battle! Neither could the captain. The doctor killed a big fellow but it was not his fault. The croc was lying on a high bank asleep. He looked like a lump of gray mud in the mangroves but the native's sharp eyes saw him instantly.

Sliding the canoe close to the bank he whispered:

"*Bwana,* there right above us. See, he sleep. You shoot him in head."

That was good advice and the doctor tried to follow it. But he wasn't at his best that morning and the bullet caught the croc midway of the tail. Things happened instantly. The reptile made a wild spring into the air and turned down for the water in a beautiful dive. It landed on the bamboo outrigger of the canoe and kept on coming, mouth open.

"*Bwana,* shoot, shoot, he eat you," screamed the Malay.

He would have eaten him too, there is no doubt about that. The doctor frantically worked the bolt of his rifle and crammed a shell into the chamber just in time. Shoving the barrel right between the gaping white jaws, he pulled the trigger. The back of the croc's head suddenly disappeared for a dumdum bullet admits of no argument when it hits bone. The doctor could touch the reptile's head where it sank down on the edge of the canoe. I was only a short distance away and paddled up to find the medico still sitting in the canoe wondering just what had happened. The croc didn't really mean to do any damage, I'm sure, but the bullet in his tail sort of unsettled his mental reactions. He just jumped and happened to land on the canoe. The natives seemed awfully keen to have the crocodiles killed for I believe they do get a good many people each year. It would be a spooky death to be quietly dragged under water by an unseen force when one was fording a stream!

For me every day of the cruise was filled to the brim with interest and excitement. To drop off on little uninhabited coral islands which perhaps had been visited but a few times even by natives; to explore them and collect strange birds and animals which I had read about but never seen; to be working in the ship's laboratory where there were always new creatures from the ocean depths; all this kept me living in a dream-world. There never were enough hours to do half the things I wanted to do. There never have been enough hours since.

I am writing these lines in my office at the American Museum of Natural History on my birthday, the twenty-sixth of January. It has been just twenty-three years since I began to wander. In the next twenty-three years I wonder if there will come a time when life is no longer a wonderful adventure; when there is not some interesting experience in things or personalities waiting just around the corner! If that time ever does come, I hope that my release will be swift.

When we returned to the Philippines, I learned something about which I had always been curious. Why is it that sailors at the end of a cruise want to raise Cain and spend every cent of the money they have worked so hard to make? I found out because that was just what I wanted to do. We had been away so long that every shop looked enticing; every girl was beautiful; all music was intoxicating. The contrast and the sudden change upset our sense of values. Moreover we were happy to be back and we had to show it or burst. It is this that sends a sailor off on a wild orgy during his first shore leave. By the time the contrast and newness wears off his money is gone, and he is a sadder but not a wiser man. He will do it all over again after his next cruise.

I have had enough long absences from civilization to conduct my celebrations with a certain amount of judgment, but I must confess that the inclination is there, almost as strong as ever. It is a natural human outlet, just as a volcano explodes when too much steam has accumulated. Therefore, please temper your judgment of the poor sailor—and explorer—with understanding.

CHAPTER VII

THE *Albatross* left Manila in January, 1910, and steamed northward dredging on the way. She touched at the Loo Choo Islands, that forgotten kingdom of the East. A kingdom once so important that Commodore Perry considered it almost as necessary to make a treaty with its ruler as with the Emperor of Japan. We saw the picturesque old Shuri Palace where the treaty had been signed.

Then northward to Formosa. We made only three stops on that little-known island, for the Japanese were having such difficulty in subduing the wild head-hunters that they would not allow us to go far inland. The Japanese official who came out to the ship from a tiny village on the southern tip of Formosa looked indescribably funny. His boat consisted of a washtub fastened to a bamboo raft. He sat in the tub dressed in full uniform, gold lace, white gloves, sword and all the rest. He tried to look dignified but it just couldn't be done. When I went ashore to collect birds he insisted that I have a guard of Japanese soldiers. One cannot make much headway shooting, with a detachment of soldiers trailing along behind, and I had to give it up.

At the tiny village of Soo Wan we got some enormous sea-turtles as large as barrels; also cakes of camphor. The place smelled so strongly of camphor that the odor was wafted to us even when the ship was well out in the bay. Soo Wan is only forty miles south of Kelung, if I remember correctly, but the *Albatross* nearly went down with all hands on board before we got there.

One of the typhoons that incubate off the Philippine coast got loose and picked upon us as a likely victim. It swept up with amazing suddenness catching us when we were half way to Kelung. I had always wanted to experience a typhoon, but never again! In the beginning we passed a small, low-lying British gun-boat. She sent a man aft presumably to hoist her colors. I was watching through my binoculars and saw a great sea suddenly lap over her stern sweeping the man off the deck like a straw. It was pretty awful seeing that man disappear so quickly into the boiling white waves! Neither did it help our peace of mind for all of us had begun to realize that the gallant old *Albatross* might not make it. In a few hours we ourselves might feel the strangling water closing over our heads. I had often wondered how I would act in such an emergency. I can't remember exactly what my feelings were but I don't think I was frightened. No one seemed to be. A tense calmness pervaded the whole ship. We were fighting a battle for life against the elements and the odds were on their side. There was very little talking for it was difficult to hear above the shrieking gale and crashing water.

We were headed directly into the seas which broke over the bow and swept the deck every time the ship dived into one of the mountainous waves. A mile away sheer cliffs rose like a wall above a narrow beach, smothered in white foam. It was a dangerous place but the captain did not dare head out to sea; apparently he thought that our one hope lay in beating against the rising typhoon to Kelung only twenty miles away. Yet for a time it seemed that the safe harbor might just as well be a thousand miles distant for often we could not even hold our own against the storm. But foot by foot the old ship crept forward, sometimes losing more than she had gained but always coming back for another attack at the smashing waves.

Just as night closed in we saw lights on our port bow. An hour later the *Albatross* limped into the outer harbor, battered and smashed but game to the last. Outside the typhoon roared past, increasing in violence every minute. Next morning during the half hour run to the inner harbor the starboard engine gave way. Had that happened before we reached shelter nothing could have saved us. It was because we knew the weakness of that particular engine that the captain had not dared to ride out into the storm on the high seas.

The *Albatross* had been so badly treated that we lay at Kelung several days making repairs; then she steamed slowly northward to Nagasakai. During my first walk through the market place of the little city I made a great discovery. Whale meat was being sold in half a dozen shops! I knew in a vague way that shore-whaling was being conducted in Japan but this tangible evidence gave me a new idea. Why not stay here and see what was what in Japanese whale life? The *Albatross* was about to start home across the Pacific; I could be of no use on her but I could do a real job here. I sent a cable to the Museum outlining my plan. The answer was "yes."

The office of the whaling company proved to be in Shimonoseki and rejoiced in the name of "Toyo

Hogei Kabushiki Kaisha," Oriental Whaling Company, Ltd. A visit proved most successful for the hospitable Japanese took kindly to the idea of a foreign scientist investigating their whales. They are keen about that sort of thing and showed it by inviting me to go where I pleased and do what I wished. I could not have had a more charming reception anywhere in the world. A few days later I said good-bye to my shipmates on the *Albatross* and boarded one of the little transport vessels of the whaling company bound for a station at Shimizu.

I could not speak a word of Japanese but I had a grammar and a dictionary besides abundant courage. I was all against hiring an interpreter. I would not learn the language half as quickly as if I had to speak it to get what I wanted. But the introduction to Japanese village life did put me in some amusing situations. For a week I lived at a tiny hotel close by the station. I arrived there in the late afternoon and found that the proprietor could speak a little copy-book English. My room was a bird-cage sort of place with clean white matting on the floor, but the whole front was open to the street which was lined with spectators. I felt just like a new arrival at the zoo. Of course my host asked immediately if I wanted a bath. I did.

"The-water-is-clean," said he, "only-five-people-have-bathed-already!"

He closed the paper screen of my room, gave me a kimono, and I proceeded to disrobe. I was lucky, for this particular bath-room happened to be enclosed. The water in the great wooden tub really was cleaner than might be expected after five baths. I was just about to step in when the door opened and my host presented a smiling girl dressed in a lovely flowered kimono.

"This-girl-will-wash-your-back," said he in his funny slow English. With a yell I leaped for my bath robe.

"Get out. I can wash my own back," I shouted, pushing both of them through the door. Ten minutes later he reappeared with a different lady.

"*This*-girl-will-wash-your-back," he repeated with a most ingratiating smile.

"I'll be hanged if she will," I roared and slammed the door again.

The next time he knocked timidly. His face was a picture of despair.

"If - you - do - not - like - my - servants - I - will - get-a-geisha," he almost wept.

Obviously I had committed a grave social error in not wishing to have my back washed by a young lady to whom I had not been introduced. I was in Japan. Better do as the Japanese do, I thought. I couldn't hurt the poor man's feelings even at the sacrifice of my own false modesty.

"Bring on your girls," said I, and the ablutions were performed to the accompaniment of many little bubbling exclamations in Japanese. Afterward I learned their meaning. It was what, in the modern flapper, would be called "a line."

"How white your skin is," most of them ran, "just like snow!"

In less than a week I was laughing with my new Japanese friends at my strange western conception of modesty where it concerns such a natural function as that of bathing.

All my meals were eaten with chop sticks and I had the usual Japanese food. An assortment of pickles, raw fish and white radish; then soup, fish, chicken or eggs and rice. Always tea, of course. I did not like it much at first but became accustomed to it soon enough.

Shimizu was not a success from the whaling standpoint as the season for that station had almost ended. Not a single whale was taken in the ten days I remained and the company suggested that I go to

THE CUSTOM HOUSE QUAY IN MANILA.

CANAL LIFE IN MANILA.

Oshima where finbacks, sulphur-bottoms and sei whales were then being killed.

Oshima was a delightful spot on an island of the Inland Sea. High above the beach perched the stationmaster's dwelling where I lived. It was like a children's play-house, all paper screens, sliding doors and spotless matting. We could look across to a dozen islands where gnarled pine trees grew at impossible angles from moss covered rocks. Everything was so new and strange that I seemed to be living in a story-book world.

There was no time for loafing here. The season was in full swing and not a day went by without at least one whale. The "cutting in" operations were totally unlike those at Vancouver and Alaska. In fact, I have seen nothing like it anywhere else in the world. At the end of a long wharf two huge poles jutted out over the water. Across the connecting bar, at the top, ran the wires from a steam winch. The dead whale lay on its side at the end of the wharf. Two men in a boat cut through the body just forward of the dorsal fin. Then the entire posterior part of the carcass was hoisted into the air and lowered on to the wharf. Men, women and girls attacked it like a swarm of ants cutting off huge chunks of meat and blubber which were drawn to a rear platform with great iron hooks. Meanwhile chains were made fast about one of the side fins or flippers and the flesh and blubber torn away as the carcass rolled over in the water.

Every whale was cut in the moment it arrived at the station no matter at what time of the night or day. There was not an hour's delay for the meat must be rushed by fast transports to the nearest large town there to be sold as food in the markets. The oil was a secondary consideration. Each whale was worth four or five times its value in America. A seventy-five foot sulphur-bottom yields forty tons of edible meat to say nothing of the blubber. At that time it was worth five thousand dollars in Japan. Humpbacks were considered to be the best eating; finbacks and sei whales not so good. Sperms worst of all. Because the meat is so dark and filled with oil it could be sold only to the poorest people.

Whale meat is really good, if properly prepared, even to Western taste. During the early part of the World War, I made an effort to introduce it into America. The Vancouver Island and Alaska companies agreed to send it to the large cities of the U. S. in refrigerator cars, if I could create a market. We gave a luncheon at the American Museum of Natural History to inaugurate the campaign.

The meat was put on sale in New York, Chicago, Seattle, San Francisco and other cities. It went well enough at first, but the expense of transporting it such long distances made the plan impracticable after the novelty wore off.

In Japan during the summer they can many thousand tons of meat. We tried that also but the American public did not take kindly to tinned whale meat. Personally, I really like it. The flavor is much like that of ordinary beef but there is a slight oily taste if it has not been previously soaked in soda or salt water. A steak cut from the tenderloin of a young humpback, smothered in onions or served with mushrooms, is distinctly good. There is another advantage too—the tenderloins are big enough even for a large family. Each one weighs about a ton.

The fibrous flukes were cut into thin strips by the Japanese, pickled in brine and sent to the markets of Tokio, Yokohama, Osaka, Kobe and other large cities. The huge rope-like tendons of the posterior part of the body, after being dried, usually went to China. The bones and viscera were tried out for oil and made into fertilizer as in America.

Almost every night the station whistles announced the arrival of a fresh whale. I always went down to the wharf not only to do my scientific work but to watch the strange scene. Flares of oil-soaked waste lighted the station yard. Men and women stripped to the waist, girls and children in blue kimonos waded through pools of shining blood, slipped on the greasy blubber and tore like demons at great chunks of steaming meat. "Ya-ra-cu-ra-sa," they sang in a meaningless chant as they strained and heaved at the colossal bones. It was all so strange, so barbaric that I could hardly believe it was happening in the year of our Lord, 1910.

Work for me was made difficult by this method of cutting in. The entire whale was seldom taken out of the water and I had to measure it in sections. Still I learned how to get the most important data before the carcass reached the hands of the devastating women.

My field was absolutely untouched. Hardly a word existed in scientific literature regarding these whales which were coming under my observation in such numbers. It was a priceless opportunity; no naturalist would ever have another like it. How I did work! There was seldom more than five or six hours of sleep for me during the twenty-four, but I was only twenty-six years old and burning with enthusiasm. When I was not on the wharf covered with blood and grease, I had quantities of notes and observations to record, photographs to develop, and specimens to prepare.

The whaling company had given me permission to take what skeletons I required. An eighty foot sulphur-bottom, a fifty foot sei whale and a killer twenty-six feet long were my first acquisitions and these had to be cleaned of flesh and carefully crated. That was no small job. I sent to Oshima for carpenters and lumber and the Japanese made me crates that could have been sent around the world and back again without breakage. But the size of the skull box for the sulphur-bottom appalled me. It was twenty-two feet long and had a space measurement of more than twenty tons. Some of the other cases were almost as big. How was I ever to get them to Kobe where they could be put aboard a steamship for New York?

The problem was solved by a typhoon. A big schooner, absolutely empty, put into the harbor to escape the storm. It seemed like a gift from Heaven, and while the gale howled outside we loaded our bones into the ship and sent her off to Kobe.

CHAPTER VIII

WHEN I made my arrangements to study at the
Japan stations I did not dream of such a haul of
specimens. They would have been valuable from any
part of the world but more particularly so because
the Japanese whales were completely unknown.
They would enable us to settle the question as to
whether or not the Pacific and Atlantic species
were different or identical. Scientists had assumed
that they were unlike because they lived in widely
separated oceans but that was an assumption based
upon no facts. I could settle the matter definitely.

I was so busy on shore that there was no opportunity to go to sea. I did not set foot on a whaling
vessel until the station closed and I went north to the
little village of Aikawa, near Matsushima, one of
the *San Kiri* or three most beautiful spots in Japan.
There were three stations in the immediate vicinity
supplied by fourteen whaling ships. The gunners
were all Norwegians whom the Japanese had hired
to teach them shore whaling methods. One of them,

Captain Larsen, I had hunted with at Kyuquot, Vancouver Island, in 1908. They were rough men but kindly and we understood each other. I was always welcome on their ships and usually at night half a dozen of us gathered at some one of the village tea houses for dinner or a *geisha* dance.

At Aikawa my home was with the station master whom I had met at Shimizu. He gave me a beautiful little doll's house next his own for myself and a tiny servant girl to administer to my physical comfort. Her name was *Kinu-san* (silk) and she looked exactly like a brilliant butterfly as she flashed about the house and gardens. Every morning she used to steal into my room with a vase of fresh flowers that I might find the new day beautiful.

Kinu-san became my nurse, too, for after a fortnight I fell ill with a strange intermittent fever. There was no doctor nearer than Tokio, three hundred miles away. I was too weak to travel there and had to do the best I could with my own limited knowledge. Usually at night I was delirious for a time and when morning came was weak and spent with fever. Kinu never left me. She became thin and strained through lack of sleep. Every day she used to go to her little tone *joss* in the temple on the hillside to pray for my recovery. And when finally the fever left me and I became strong enough to walk again she asked that I, too, should go with her to thank the god. Not for worlds would I had said her nay. The whaling captains were kind, as rough men can be. Each one brought me gifts of some delicacy from his private store. Then Captain Andersen took me off with him for a week at sea.

The weather was fine and sei whales plentiful. They had just arrived in these waters following up the coast with the warmth of summer. The sei is one of the smaller species, seldom reaching a greater length than fifty feet. In Norway it is called the sardine whale. Doubtless there it does eat small fish but in Japan shrimps were its food. It is a beautiful animal, light gray in color, sometimes with a tinge of pink. They are not hard to kill, as whales go, but one nearly wrecked the ship. Andersen had sent a harpoon crashing into its side and the great body slowly sank. He thought it was dead and gave the order to heave it up with the winch. At the first turn of the wheels the line began to rise, tense and rigid as a bar of steel. Suddenly the whale burst to the surface, whirled about and dashed straight at the ship.

"Hard a port, he'll sink us," yelled Andersen dancing about like a mad man.

The helmsman swung the wheel just in time. The whale struck a glancing blow, scraped along the vessel's side and ran its nose into the propeller. The whirling blades tore off huge strips of flesh and blubber. Backing away the animal swam parallel with us, its whole head out of water. Then rolling on its side, with the great fin in the air, it gave a convulsive twist and sank.

The charge was not premeditated. It was not a direct attack on the ship but only the death flurry. Nevertheless, had it struck us squarely the vessel's side would have been ripped like paper. Thirty tons of bone and muscle coming at twenty knots an hour can do a good deal of damage even to a steel ship. I know of several that have been sunk that way. All of them were in the flurry though the sperm whale sometimes does attack a boat with real malice.

I was amazed at the rapidity with which sharks gathered as soon as a whale was killed. It seemed to make no difference where we were, whether close to shore or far out at sea. By the time a whale had been hauled to the surface huge gray-green shadows were darting about, now and then showing a flash of white as they turned to bite. I suppose it was the blood that brought them but how could they find it so quickly? The ocean, off the Japan coast, must swarm with sharks.

There is not much about a shark to love. I loathed them. They are cannibalistic beasts for whenever I shot one with a rifle it was torn in bits by its fellows before it had time to sink. The gunners said that they would not attack a man but I was in the water once with sharks all about me and I felt far from comfortable. We were fast to a big fin-back whale which continued to be so lively that the ship could not approach near enough for another shot. The mate went out in a small pram to lance the beast and I asked to pull the stern oar. The whale was lying at the surface blowing frequently. We slid up quietly almost touching the enormous back which looked like the deck of a submarine. As the mate thrust the slender steel into the body, the great flukes rose and fell with one tremendous crash. Just the tip caught the stern of the boat crushing it like an egg-shell. Before I knew what had happened the three of us were in the water clinging to the floating wreckage.

Hundreds of sharks had been following the blood trail of the wounded whale. They swarmed about our feet. I actually kicked one in the nose but he only backed off and made no turn to bite. I suppose

BIG BULL SEAL WITH HIS FAMILY: ST. PAUL'S ISLAND.

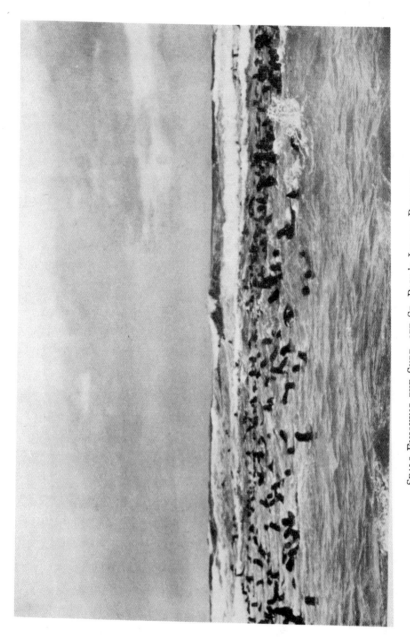

Seals Enjoying the Surf, off St. Paul's Island Rookery.

it was because we were living creatures and a shark feeds largely upon dead things. Still one might have wished to change his diet and these sharks were fifteen feet long!

In July and August sperm whales follow up this coast but keep well out to sea. They are seldom nearer shore than one hundred and fifty miles. Captain Fred Olsen had promised to kill a really big sperm if he could find one because I particularly wanted a skeleton for the Museum.

Half a dozen were brought in during the first week of August but they were all females or young males, none being more than forty-seven feet long. In the toothed whales the cows are much smaller than the bulls; the opposite is true of the baleen whales. The station was to be closed by August 15, and the big sperm had not materialized. I was in despair. Then Captain Olsen said, "I'll go far out tomorrow and see what I can find. I'll not bother with a small one."

He was gone three days and returned with a sixty foot sperm, a magnificent bull, battle scarred, white with age. The old veteran was hard to kill and Olsen had fired four harpoons into the body but not a bone was broken by the exploding bombs.

A sperm whale is an amazing beast for the great

head is rectangular, instead of pointed. The upper two-thirds of the head is devoted to an immense tank in which the oil, called spermaceti, floats in a liquid condition. When a hole has been cut the oil can be dipped out with buckets. "Bailing the case" whalemen call it. I am not certain, but I believe that we took fourteen barrels of spermaceti from this big bull.

There has been considerable argument as to the function of the case but I am sure that it is a reservoir for the storage of nourishment. During a shortage of food the animal can absorb the oil just as do seals and bears. When a bear hibernates he goes into his winter bed simply rolling in fat. This is absorbed during the long sleep and he needs no food. A camel lives on his "hump" in the same way. Last summer when my caravan started into the western Gobi Desert their humps were hard and firm, standing up like small mountains of fat. Those camels that returned after weeks of thirst and hunger had flapping humps like empty sacks.

After the sperm whale's skull was crated it alone had a space measurement of fourteen tons. I had a big finback skeleton, a dozen porpoises and many tubs of fish. The collection from Aikawa measured eighty tons. We got the huge crates to Matsushima where they were put on a vessel for Yokohama. You may see the skeleton today in the new Hall of Ocean Life at the American Museum of Natural History.

During the summer which I spent at Aikawa I came to know every man, woman and child in the little fishing village. I was a curiosity to them and they were just as interesting to me. Nothing I did escaped comment. I had about as much privacy as a gold fish. But still no one had any privacy. It wasn't considered either necessary or polite. The most intimate functions of the toilette were carried on in full view of the passers by. The public bath house was a meeting place for gossip and news. It happened to be on the main street of the village and I often saw girls standing at the entrance clothed in considerably less than the modern woman wears at a bathing beach. But how they did "oh" and "ah" and blush over pictures in American magazines showing women in *décolleté* evening dress. They never would have worn clothes like that. It was too awful; most frightfully immodest. I could speak Japanese fairly well by that time and they told me in no uncertain terms what they thought of some of our customs.

I came to understand, too, how inherently polite

Japanese are. It is not just on the surface; it is congenital. The charming little phrases with which one was met at the door of a village hotel protesting the humbleness of the entertainment; the sweet greeting of my little servant kneeling in the door when I returned after a day's absence; meaningless and exaggerated one might say, if taken literally, but delightful nevertheless. Would that we had more of that and less matter-of-factness in our own life. We would all be better for it.

Since there was no doctor in the village and I had a medical kit, I did a rushing business. Most of my patients had diseases which could be cured with antiseptics but I always had to give internal medicine as well whether it was necessary or not. They would not follow directions otherwise. The more evil a concoction tasted the more certain they were of its effectiveness. I prepared a stock solution of colored water and quinine, bitter as gaul but harmless. It was amazing what cures it made.

I removed teeth, cut off a man's hand that had been crushed in the winch, treated dozens of cases of eczema and officiated at the birth of two babies. All this on what I had learned of comparative anatomy in the College of Physicians and Surgeons, New York, two years earlier. It was pretty sketchy knowledge to work upon, but better than none at all. At any rate not one of my patients died and many recovered. What qualified specialist can say as much!

When the station at Aikawa closed and my eighty tons of skeletons were on their way to New York, I went to Shimonoseki to collect fish. Steam trawling was then a recent introduction in Japan, and Shimonoseki was the center of the industry. There were only fifteen or twenty foreigners in the city including a single American, Dr. Houston. I think all the rest were British.

The ports of China and Japan in those days were pretty wild. Wine, women and song seemed to be the real *raison d' être* of life. Business was done casually when it did not interfere with pleasure. Shimonoseki rejoiced in the reputation of being the hardest drinking port in the East. That was superlative and I was perfectly willing to have my share of fun, but I wanted to take it in my own way. I had a job which was the most important thing in life to me and I did not intend to offer it as a sacrifice at the bar of the Shimonoseki club. Therefore, instead of living at the hotel, I got myself a house a mile out of the city where I could be alone. It was a sweet little place set high up in a pocket of the hills overlooking the entrance to the Inland Sea. I rented it for thirty *yen* (fifteen dollars) a month. This also included a man, his wife and daughter, a cat, four gold fish and a frog. The Japanese couple with their daughter lived in a back room; the cat and I had the front of the house; the gold fish and frog resided in a pool of the garden spanned by a tiny red-lacquer bridge.

I was extraordinarily happy there. At night I watched the sun set over the Inland Sea and the shipping of the Straits. Great ocean liners slipped through the narrow channel, sampans, square-rigged fishing boats, launches and stubby trawlers. As darkness gathered the strumming of a *samisen*, feminine laughter, the soft notes of a bamboo flute floated up from a tea house below the hill. Then my frog began his nightly serenade. Yes, those days were very happy ones.

Every morning I went first to the docks where the trawlers brought their fish. I looked them over buying what I wanted and then proceeded to the general markets. The old women at the stands soon came to know me well and saved every unusual specimen. Some even gambled by buying strange fish that were not very good to eat in hopes that I might want them.

134

The sharks were particularly interesting and of great variety. The fins and tails were dried for export to China; the large species skinned for leather; the smaller ones kept for food. I preserved my fish in formalin and soon had a splendid collection. I have forgotten how many different species were represented but it was well over a hundred.

When I no longer had an excuse to remain in Japan I cabled the Museum that I was starting home but not to expect me soon. I had sent back enormous collections and I planned to wander a bit before I reached New York. I wanted to see all the biggest museums of Europe and England; to learn how they compared with ours in America.

From Japan I went to Peking and had the first sight of the city which has since been my home for many years. The Emperor was on the Dragon throne; the Forbidden City, a place of intrigue and mystery. In the famous old Wagon Lits, the "Hotel of the Six Nations" a strange new world passed before my eyes. Manchu princes and gorgeous ladies with rouged cheeks; men and women of every nationality; an atmosphere of politics and diplomacy. Only a year later those same resplendent nobles were fleeing for their lives, the Emperor was deposed and China had entered upon a reign of republican chaos from which it will not emerge for many years to come. Peking fascinated me. Even then, with no definite plans, I said to myself, "here I will live some day."

Then Shanghai and a beautiful German ship to carry me southward; one of the North German Lloyd—I have forgotten her name. Hongkong, and Singapore, a new view of the tropics; Ceylon, a paradise on earth, and on through the steaming Red Sea.

My ticket read to Naples but at Port Said I felt a sudden urge to look at Egypt. My heavy baggage had all been sent to New York and I had only two large suit cases. In one my evening clothes and warmer things; in the other half a dozen white suits which take little room. That is the way to travel if one really wishes to see the world. Have no definite plans and no impedimenta. Jump off the ship or train wherever a place looks interesting and stay until it bores you.

Egypt and the Sahara were fascinating. It was the first desert I had ever seen and I loved it. I made a vow, which has since come true, to live in a desert and learn its mystery. After Egypt came Europe from Italy north to Hamburg and back again to Paris and London. Always wandering with no definite plans, free to follow the wish of the moment, ever on the lookout for adventures, either in things or personalities. I never failed to find them. Some were good and some were bad but all were interesting. By the time I reached New York plans were ready in my mind for another visit to the Orient. The lure of the East was strong upon me. Before a year had passed I was at sea again headed for Korea.

CHAPTER IX

WHILE I was in Japan in 1910 I heard of a strange whale called the *koku kujira,* or devilfish, which was being taken off the Korean coast. The description sounded much like the California gray whale. But the gray whale had been extinct for fifty years—at least as far as naturalists were aware. The animals used to come into the California lagoons to breed. There they were hunted relentlessly and eventually disappeared.

I thought a good deal about this Korean devilfish on the way back to America. Either it was an animal entirely new to science or else the lost gray whale. Perhaps I would have the opportunity to rediscover a supposedly extinct species!

Plans were ready in my mind when I reached New York. I said "how do you do?" to President Osborn at the Museum and at the same time asked permission to go back to the Orient. It was not difficult to convince him; he saw immediately the importance of what I proposed.

138

The devilfish appear twice a year along the Korean coast; when they go northward in the spring and again in the autumn upon their return journey to warmer waters. That much I knew from reports and the whaling company records. Therefore, I planned to reach Korea in January to be ready for the spring migration.

It meant that I would have less than a year in New York but that would be quite enough. The fires of "wanderlust" were hot within me and I knew that I should be wild to seek the open road before the year was out.

That winter and summer were busy ones. I resumed my interrupted work at Columbia University; described several strange new porpoises which I had collected in Japan and was appointed an assistant curator in the Museum. Shortly afterward I was visiting at the house of a friend. His ten-year-old daughter introduced me to a guest as follows:

"This is Mr. Andrews, Assistant *Creator* of Mammals in the American Museum of Natural History."

I was very proud of my new title. Now I am a curator-in-chief, but I never have had time to "curate" much since my first year in the Museum.

In order to curate properly a curator must stay at home—at least some of the time. I couldn't do it. I never returned from an expedition without having plans for another ready to submit to President Osborn at our first interview. I have found that it is wise to strike while the iron is hot. The enthusiasm of one's return from a successful trip carries great weight in the plans for a new one. Then again I was always afraid that I would get so immersed in Museum affairs that the authorities might think I had better stay at home for awhile. If the new trip had been approved and was in the offing it was much easier to keep my particular decks clear for action. Not that I did not like Museum work. On the contrary I loved it. The Museum had come to be a part of myself, and there was no phase of the activities in the great institution that did not fascinate me. But I loved wandering more. Sometimes when I walked across the Park on a starlit summer's night I used to look up at the drifting clouds, going with them in imagination far out to sea into strange new worlds. Then I would count the days that still remained before I could set my feet upon the unknown trails that led Eastward to the Orient.

There was hardly a night that I left my office

BASKING IN THE SUN AT ST. PAUL'S ISLAND ROOKERY.

SEALS GOING FROM THE ROOKERY INTO THE SURF.

in the Museum before one o'clock in the morning. I had so much to do and so few hours in which to do it that I hated to waste any of them in sleep. I was always writing something, either scientific papers or articles for magazines, and I worked best at night. When the vast halls of the Museum were still and shadows played about the books and specimens in my office, my mind was clearest.

Shortly after the whaling trip to Alaska I had written my first article for a great magazine. It was for *World's Work*, and that brought me into contact with Mr. Walter Page who later became Ambassador to the Court of St. James's. His fatherly interest in my doings, his kindly criticisms and suggestions influenced me more deeply than I dreamed of at the time. Once, with considerable pride, I showed an article to Mr. Page. He looked at it and said:

"I can hardly understand a sentence of all this. Why couldn't you have written it in non-technical language. Your audience would be so much larger. Remember that science which is sufficient unto itself has no excuse for being."

That thought remained in my mind. When I had discovered something really interesting and important why express it in phraseology which only trained investigators could understand? Of course like all youngsters in science I loved to use technical terms. It made me feel very learned. But I soon abandoned that attitude, and when it was necessary to write a paper in technical language for a first presentation, I re-phrased it later.

The winter and summer of 1911 were gone almost before I realized that they had begun. Just eleven months after my return to New York I sailed again from San Francisco for the Orient. I was on the *Shinyo Maru,* a new ship of the Toyo Kissen Kaisha then making her maiden voyage across the Pacific. We had Christmas at sea. The Japanese did us very well. I think few of the passengers ever will forget that trip. As for myself, certain details remain clear and distinct in my mind even after eighteen years!

I knew that the "devilfish" hunt would be ended in March but I had no intention of returning to the Museum then. Far from it. I determined to explore the forests of Northern Korea along the Manchurean border which then remained virtually unknown. In 1879 Sir Francis Younghusband had made his first expedition with James and Fulford to the Long White Mountain. From the summit they had looked across the Korean forests and wondered what lay within. Then, Korea was a Hermit Kingdom. He who crossed its borders risked death or imprisonment.

In 1911 all this was changed. The Japanese had annexed the country after the war of 1904, and were rapidly extending their influence to the uttermost confines of the new province. I made up my mind to be the first to tell the Western world what lay in the solitude of the Korean wilderness.

A short stay in Yokohama, Kobe and Shimonoseki to greet old friends; then on a little meat-transport steamer *en route* to the station north of Fusan on the Eastern Korean coast. It was like others I had visited and set in a picturesque bay among the treeless, scrub-covered hills. The employees were all Japanese but dozens of Koreans swarmed on the dock as we drew alongside.

Interesting people dressed in long white gowns and wearing tiny horsehair hats. A veritable "Happy Hooligan" headgear but in spite of it the men seemed strangely dignified. Women in voluminous white skirts with bright colored sashes and jackets so short that their naked breasts appeared beneath. Some girls were really lovely; delicate oval faces, skins almost white and soft brown eyes. To a Westerner the Korean girls are much prettier than either the Chinese or Japanese women. I suppose because their features more nearly approximate our own.

In proper Korean family life the women's apartment is inviolate. No one but a husband, brother or father is allowed to enter. Even a policeman searching for a criminal would not go into the women's rooms except under direct necessity. If a neighbor was obliged to ascend to the roof of his house, in courtesy he was bound to warn those on either side so that the women might withdraw indoors. Custom decrees that the women may expose their faces and breasts without offense, but nothing else. Dresses almost sweep the ground. Eyes straight to the front or modestly cast down when a stranger passes. Still they had curiosity enough about me. Whenever I walked through the village near the whaling station I would see fingers pushing holes in the paper windows and hear the gurgling sounds of laughter.

The Korean woman is by no means a spiritless person. She is a most efficient housewife, in her own peculiar way, and pretty well bosses friend-husband as well as all the other male relations. But she has little to say about choosing a mate. Often she is married when only ten or twelve years old to

The Korean Expedition's Second Camp.

DEER SHOT BY ANDREWS IN THE KOREAN FOREST.

a boy of like age. The happy couple spend a few nights together and then return to their own homes until such time as their parents deem them fit to reside permanently in conjugal bliss.

Bachelors are not encouraged in Korea. When a boy is married he ties up his hair in a knot on the top of his head and dons the horse-hair hat. He is then referred to as a "man" no matter what his age. Until he is married he must keep his hair in a braid and may not wear a hat. Even though he should be fifty years old he is always a "boy" and has no voice in community affairs.

This much and more I learned the first day at the whaling station, for I have an insatiable curiosity about the customs of a new people. I could speak Japanese fairly well and one of the young clerks at the station knew a little English. I am afraid I exhausted him with my ceaseless questioning but he was invariably polite.

Because the Japanese were away from home more freedom was allowed the men. When no whales were in, Japanese *geisha* and Korean "sing-song" girls flocked about the station. It was a very merry place. Everyone seemed to be having a good time. At night I was lulled to sleep by the distant sounds of a twanging *samisen* and feminine laughter.

But the moment the station whistles roared out the call of approaching whales all pleasure ceased. Flares appeared like magic throwing a fitful light over the long dock and the still black water of the bay. In ten minutes I had pulled on my long boots and heavy coat. It was bitterly cold outside. The whale ship *Main*, shrouded in ice from stem to stern, swept proudly into the bay and slipped up to the crowded wharf.

From her bow drooped the huge black flukes of a whale. My great moment had come. I was to find a species new to science or rediscover one that had been lost for half a century! Either prospect was exciting enough to set my pulses leaping. In this day and age one doesn't discover a great new animal every Tuesday and Thursday! If it were the lost California gray whale what a chance I had to write the story of its wanderings since it had disappeared from Western knowledge.

First glance showed that the flukes differed in shape from any that I had ever seen; also they were marked with strange gray circles. When the cutters had hacked through the body and the posterior part came slowly into view I saw that the back was finless and the dorsal edge strongly crenulated. Up came a wide stubby flipper; a short arched head.

Those told the story. It was the gray whale without a doubt. I got all I could in the darkness and retired to the *futon* on the floor of my tiny paper-screened room. But not to sleep. I was too excited. After vainly trying for half an hour, I lit a candle and spent the remainder of the night checking up every detail of what I had seen with Scammon's account written almost twenty years before I was born. Scammon had given the only existing picture of the gray whale. My observations of the external anatomy matched his point for point.

In the first gray light of dawn I went out to the wharf to examine what was left of the whale. Only the head and flippers remained. All the rest, except the viscera, had been loaded into the meat-transport the night before and was already half across the Japan Sea. But at eleven o'clock the siren-whistle of another whale-ship sounded twice down the bay announcing the arrival of two more devilfish. The station-master, interested in my work, gave me ample time to measure and describe the whales before they were torn apart by the cutters. It was a really satisfactory day. That night I was so tired that even an invitation to a *geisha* dinner and dance could not tempt me from the *futons*.

During the next six weeks I examined more than

forty gray whales; saw them hunted by men and killers; learned their clever tricks to avoid both these deadly enemies; and pieced together bit by bit the story of their wanderings.

The days at sea were torture. Always heavy weather and deathly sickness for me; bitter cold, sleet and ice. Standing behind the gun for hours on end, my oilskins stiff from frozen spray, I used to curse the sea. Why had I deliberately chosen a job which took me off the land!

But hardly was I back on shore transcribing my wealth of new data before the suffering was forgotten and I was keen to go out again.

Briefly, the story of the lost gray whale is this: There were two migration routes from the Arctic Ocean; one Southward along the American coast, the other closely following that of Asia. The gray whale is a shore-loving species and seeks the sheltered lagoons in which to drop its young. Constant persecution on its breeding-grounds had virtually exterminated the American herd. The numbers were so reduced that it was no longer profitable to hunt those whales. Probably a few continued to visit California yearly but as no ships came there they remained unreported. During the half century

KOREAN FISHER-FOLK WITH THEIR NETS.

A Peaceful Pipe in Korea.

of peace their numbers increased so that within the last few years they are again being killed.

The other herd which summers in the Okhotsk Sea and further North comes Southward close along the shore as far down as the Yellow Sea. It had not been molested until the Japanese began their whaling operations and scientists were not aware of its existence.

The valuable fur seal has a similar story. Asiatic and American herds which do not mingle in the North.

I got two gray whale skeletons at the Korean station. One went to the American Museum of Natural History, and the other to the U. S. National Museum. My study revealed that this is a very primitive species. It is almost a living fossil. Back in the Pliocene age, six or seven millions of years ago, lived a whale which is its direct ancestor. From the standpoint of zoölogy the gray whale is the most important of all existing cetaceans.

When I got my first skeleton, the bones were partially cleaned and piled in the yard only a short distance from my house. Signs "Do not touch" were posted about it. Nevertheless when I checked up the skeleton I found parts of it missing. I suspected the Koreans who were continually loafing about the station and set myself to watch. I saw two of them steal up and slip away with a bone. This happened several times and I discovered that my whale was slowly being boiled for soup. In fact so many bones had disappeared already that I had to scrap that skeleton and get another. Especial warnings were issued this time, but I made up my mind to take heroic measures. I had a .22 calibre rifle and a quantity of B. B. caps for killing small birds. These were just about powerful enough to penetrate the thick, cotton-wadded trousers of a Korean.

I punched a hole through the paper screen near my writing table and before many hours saw a Korean edging in towards the skeleton. I waited until he stooped over to pick up a bone, drew a fine bead on the rear portion of his anatomy and let him have it. How that Korean did jump! If he could duplicate it in the New York Hippodrome he would make his everlasting fortune. Yelling like mad he dashed up the hill. I'll wager that he took his meals standing for several days. Anyway the news spread that that skeleton was loaded and no more bones disappeared.

I became great friends with Captain Melson, owner and captain of the S.S. *Main*. He ran his own vessel and killed whales on commission. It was profitable for he was an experienced hunter and a magnificent shot. Today he owns a great fleet of ships operating in South Georgia waters. His vessel was as clean and well kept as an ocean liner and his table almost as good. I supplied him with pheasants, hares, ducks and geese for the shooting was superb. At night when no whales were in, we wandered about the village, dined in tea houses, or had parties on his ship. Altogether it was a wonderful six weeks for me. I stayed on until the station closed; then crossed to Japan to ship my skeletons.

CHAPTER X

In the middle of March I went up to Seoul, the capital of Korea. Seoul resembled nothing so much as an American mining town amid Oriental surroundings. Lontag's Hotel was the gathering place for dozens of men in from the gold mines. Most of these were operated by Americans. The Club occupied a building of the former king's palace where there was a fascinating air of ruined splendor. One did very much as one pleased for the Japanese had taken over the country so recently that there were very few restrictions.

The government authorities were cordial to my proposed trip and offered to furnish me with a Japanese interpreter who spoke Korean and a little English. For obvious reasons it was wise to accept but when he turned up at the hotel I was rather astonished. He was dressed in a frock coat, much too big, and a badly ruffled silk hat. I explained that we were going on a trip of real exploration into an

unknown region; that we would wear rough shirts
and high boots, not frock coats and silk hats. That
did not deter him. As a matter of fact, he proved
to be an excellent man. He stuck by me when
things looked pretty black and I developed a real
affection for him.

In Seoul I learned all I could about the border
scouting but it was almost nothing. No one had
been in the great forests, or even seen them. With
a little cook, named Kim, and my Japanese interpreter, I sailed from Fusan up the East coast of
Korea to the village of Leshin.

There the natives were catching and drying fish
for the favorite Korean dish, called *kimshi*. It is
pretty awful. I have yet to find any native concoction which approaches it in general undesirableness.
First a fish is soaked in water until he smells to
heaven; then onions and garlic are added with a
great quantity of red pepper. When a Korean has
been eating *kimshi* the only place for him is far far
away in the great open spaces!

Trucking is by cart to the ancient half-ruined
city of Musan; on the Manchurian border we came
to the last outpost of Japanese soldiers. I spent
three weeks in the vicinity hunting a tiger which
was harrying the villages. Already it had killed

half a dozen children and hardly a day passed that some tearful peasant did not report a new loss to the gendarmes. They welcomed me with open arms. Would I kill the tiger? I would be a public benefactor! There was nothing I was more anxious to do than just that and they gave me a fine old hunter, Paik. He had received the honorable title of *sontair* because he belonged to the guild of those Koreans who had killed a tiger.

The animal hunted in a region of about fifty square miles. We could only sit tight until he was reported at some village on his beat. News came shortly and we hurried away. A girl had been the victim. We viewed the remains which were not pleasant to look upon. But the tiger had disappeared and next was heard from thirty miles away. A hard day's march over the mountains brought us to the village. Again he had left and I made another fast trek of twenty-five miles trying to cut him off. As bad luck would have it, he had gone in the opposite direction.

This marching and counter-marching continued for ten days. Finally we both arrived in a village at the same time. I had hardly made camp in a tiny Korean house before a native appeared almost incoherent with excitement. He had seen the tiger go into a cave not two miles away. It was only ten o'clock in the morning and Paik said he was as good as ours already. Late in the afternoon he would surely come out for a night raid. We would watch at the entrance to the cave.

It was a small hole about four feet high near the summit of a rocky, limestone hill. Great pug marks, very fresh, showed at the entrance. The tiger was there without a doubt.

All day we waited concealed near the mouth of the cave. Nothing happened and we spent a watchful night. Once there was the faintest sound of a rolling pebble but the tiger did not show himself. He must have caught our scent in the light wind. In the morning Paik announced that since the tiger would not come out we would crawl in and kill him where he slept. He had shot two that way with his old muzzle loading gun.

Emphatically that method did not appeal to me. I had not lost any tigers in that cave. But Paik patiently explained that I had an electric flash lamp; that the tiger would not charge the light; that if I was afraid he would take my rifle and go in alone.

I couldn't stand that. To have an old Korean calmly say that he would do my job if I was afraid was just a bit too much. We prepared to go in. I don't mind saying that I was badly frightened. There was not room enough to crawl side by side so I went first on hands and knees. Paik followed flashing the light ahead of us. A sickish smell of bones and rotting meat rose from a mass of débris in a small chamber twenty feet from the entrance, but there was no tiger. We paused to look about and discovered a passage turning sharply to the left. Paik said the tiger must be there. My scalp began to prick and a cold sweat broke out all over my body but Paik was as calm as a May morning. I got a new grip on my strained nerves and we turned the corner. Nothing but the rocky walls of a winding passage turning slightly downward! A little further and we saw a faint glimmer of daylight which became larger as we advanced. It was another entrance, or exit, from the cave on the other side of the hill-crest. We emerged among a chaotic mass of boulders where pug marks plainly showed in the soft sand. They were leading outward. I was terribly disappointed, but secretly relieved. Of course I loudly bemoaned our fate and Paik did not suspect how thoroughly frightened I had been. The Koreans in the village were not aware of the second entrance to the cave. It had long been known as a tiger-lair and nothing would induce them to go near

Junks Being Towed Up the Yalu River: Korea.

One of the Party Shoots an Alligator on a Korean River.

the summit of the hill. Had we suspected its existence it would have been easy enough to block the entrance with a boulder. The tiger had scented us when he came to the opening of the cave and had slipped out the back door without waiting to say "good bye." We heard of him again next day at a village twenty miles to the south. He was the Great Invisible, everywhere but nowhere.

Once again we thought we had him lying out in a thick grass-jungle on the flat top of a little hill. A Korean came breathlessly into camp saying that he had seen a great beast go into the grass while he was cutting wood.

Gathering twenty natives with pans and gongs we started to drive the place. I had given them explicit instructions not to begin until I reached a knoll which overlooked the patch of jungle. But in their excitement they started to beat while I was still on the level in the high grass. Suddenly there was a terrific rush and a huge animal lunged straight at me. I fired quickly. The beast rolled over but in a second it was up again and I was looking almost into the tiny bloodshot eyes of an enormous wild boar. Foam dripped from the great gnashing tusks. It was no false motion. He meant business. The second bullet caught him in the neck and he fell not five feet from the end of my rifle.

The Koreans were almost as pleased as they would have been had I killed the tiger. They are much afraid of wild boar and not without reason for I saw several natives who had received terrible wounds. I may say that this is the only unwounded animal that ever deliberately charged me.

We did not get the tiger. For three weeks I hunted him persistently, but he was a better traveler than I was. Completely exhausted from hard going and lack of sleep, I had to give him up. I might have killed him the next day, or never. It is that way in this kind of hunting. One has to outguess the beast or have luck very much on one's side.

In 1923, Kermit Roosevelt had much the same experiences in Kare, south of where I was hunting. When he reached Peking he related a tale which might almost have been my own experience with the exception of the cave episode. Kermit agreed with me that the Korean tiger richly deserves the name of the Great Invisible.

At Musan I engaged eight diminutive Korean ponies and four men for the trip into the border wilderness. The Koreans did not want to go. They never had been there and were frightened. It would have been impossible to obtain a caravan without the assistance of the Japanese gendarmes. They ordered the men to go. The ponies carried our camp equipment and food; all of us walked.

It was only fifty or sixty miles to the edge of the forests. There I camped for a few days trying to get information, but it was useless. None of the natives had been more than a few miles into the wilderness. My Koreans were sad looking men when we started Northward. Every few miles they stopped to build tiny shrines of birch bark, leave little offerings of food, and pray to their own particular gods for protection from the unknown terrors which awaited them. I took compass directions laying a course straight for the Long White Mountain—Paik-to-san the Koreans call it. The first day's march was fairly easy, up a broad valley through a thin larch forest. The second not so good. By the middle of the third afternoon we were fairly in the wilderness and making slow progress. The forest was dense, the ground littered with moss grown logs and spongy from underground water. At the end of the fourth march I camped two days for the men were very tired and much depressed. I thought a rest, fresh meat, if I could find game, would revive their spirits. Luck was with me and I killed a bear. That bear haunts me yet, for I did not give the poor brute a chance. It was almost murder. He came ambling along while I was resting on a fallen tree. Totally unconscious of my presence he walked to within thirty feet of me. The bullet caught him squarely in the heart, and my one consolation is that he never knew what happened.

The bear did much to improve the morale of my men. The paws are a great delicacy and they feasted like children forgetting for a time that they were far from home and mother.

For many days we did not see another sign of life. The forest became denser at every mile with more swamps and surface water. Time after time our ponies were mired and had to be lifted out of the mud. Lush ferns and rank grass made walking dangerous. The trees were interlaced with great festoons of gray "Spanish moss" which formed a thick canopy overhead. Down where we were there was only a gloomy half light occasionally shot through with patches of thin sun. No sounds broke the stillness except the calls of the men. No birds or animals, not even a squirrel. To make matters worse it began to rain. Not a hard refreshing rain, but a dull drizzle which continued for a week.

The men were completely disheartened, frightened at the gloomy stillness of the forest and exhausted by strenuous work. They began to talk furtively among themselves and when we camped were ominously silent if I passed their fire. The interpreter told me that they were planning to desert that night with the ponies and food, leaving us to die or get back as best we could. He had overheard their talk the previous evening. It would have been fairly serious to be left without the caravan. I could find my way out easily enough but no game meant probable starvation.

We were only two days' march from the base of the Paik-to-san and I had determined to complete my traverse against all odds. To leave it in mid-air meant that all our efforts were wasted. I told the men that we must reach the mountain; that I would give them double wages; further, that I should watch at night and if any one touched a pony he would be shot without mercy.

They did not like it much. My ultimatum was received in silence. The interpreter and I watched by turns through the night. Now and then one of the men got up to replenish the fire but they made no move to leave the camp. The next night was a repetition of the first. Both the Japanese and myself were utterly exhausted from lack of sleep and hard work. We wondered if we could stick it out another twenty-four hours.

In the late afternoon we emerged into a great burned track and the mountain rose majestically right in front of us. Banked to the top with snow it looked like a great white cloud that had settled to earth for a moment's rest.

The open sky and the mountain acted like magic on my men. They began to talk and sing and call to each other in laughing voices. I knew then that the strain was over; they would not desert me. That night we camped in the shadow of the mountain well out in the burned area beside a pond of snow water. I slept for fifteen hours, utterly exhausted.

In the later afternoon I shot a roe deer, and that completed the contentment of our party. One cannot wonder at the fears of the men. They knew that our objective was the Long White Mountain but it seemed hopeless that we could get there. They had never seen a compass. To them we were merely wandering aimlessly through the forest. When we actually arrived, and all by means of that little disk with the turning needle, their admiration knew no bounds. Of course they did not understand how it worked, but it had brought us to the Paik-to-san and that was good enough for them. They would follow anywhere I wished to go; now they had complete confidence that I would not leave them to starve in a gloomy wilderness.

Four days at the Long White Mountain was sufficient. It was futile to attempt the ascent for the snow was piled in great drifts from base to crown. But in any case there would have been little to be gained for James and Younghusband had reached the crater from the Manchurian side. My object had been to find what lay within that Korean wilderness over which they had looked thirty-three years ago. I had a compass line straight through the forest to the base and a rough map of the surrounding country.

I determined not to return by the way we had come but to strike through the forest to the headwaters of the Yalu River which could not be far to the West. It was a difficult trip; just about like what we had experienced on the way to the mountain. Dense forests, swamps and drizzling rain. But the men pushed on with light hearts laughing at difficulties and hard work, supremely confident that my little compass knew the way.

We discovered a beautiful lake set like a jewel amid the green larch forest, its shores a gray line of volcanic ash. Nearby were two large ponds swarming with mallard ducks. I shot three roe deer, a wild boar and trapped many small mammals. Birds were everywhere; flowers made a brilliant carpet in the park-like openings of the forest. I should have liked to spend a month at this delightful spot but food was running low.

A day before we reached the Yalu, while hunting roe deer, I stumbled into the camp of eight Manchurian bandits; tall, brown, hard-bitten fellows armed with long flintlock rifles. I suspected immediately what they were but they saw me as quickly as I saw them. My rifle did not help any. They had me covered from several directions. There was nothing to do but bluff it out. Fortunately I knew a little Chinese. I said I was a friend, laid down my rifle and advanced.

After a little they resumed eating and offered me tea and millet. Then they went to my camp. They looked over all our stuff but there was absolutely nothing they could use except my rifle. I told the cook to get busy as he never had before and prepare a dinner of roe deer meat. The bandits were pleased and accepted the invitation to eat with alacrity. My

A Pack Horse Founders and Falls on a Boggy Korean Trail.

PICNIC WITH THE NATIVES: KOREA.

interpreter could speak bad Chinese but enough to tell them all about us.

After dinner the brigands became most friendly. They admitted that they were part of a band which held this region near the Yalu. All merchants sending goods between villages must pay them taxes. As we were not merchants and had been so hospitable they would charge us nothing. Moreover they told us how to avoid others of the band who might not be as friendly.

The next day we camped on the bank of the great river which at that spot was less than thirty yards across. Following down the stream for two days we came to a Korean settlement. There was great rejoicing among my men for they were heroes. Had they not been to the Long White Mountain, faced the terrors of the unknown wilderness and all with the aid of a tiny compass? If I had given it to them they would certainly have placed it in a shrine to worship as a god. Every villager came to see it. Reverently they passed it about, the old men wagging their heads and saying little; the younger explaining volubly how it worked.

Further down the river we came to the first logging operations conducted by the Japanese. Here I dismissed my caravan for I had intended to float down the Yalu on a log raft. It was very comfortable on the raft. The men made me a little house of bark and I had a huge deck for a playground. Sometimes at night we tied up to a bank but usually the raft floated on guided by two men with huge sweeps. I shot ducks and geese for specimens retrieving them in a small boat towed behind the raft.

I watched the Yalu grow with every mile for we passed dozens of small streams, each of which contributed its share to swell the giant river. The trip was very restful after the strenuous days of continued travel which we had undergone. With plenty of birds and fish, I lived like a king.

But I was a sorry sight in the way of garments when we reached Antung at the mouth of the river. My shoes and trousers had completely gone. I was dressed in Korean clothes except for coat and hat. In this garb I reached Seoul and registered at the Lontag Hotel.

A cable to the Museum elicited a delightful reply. For nearly five months I had dropped out of the world and the usual reports of death in the Korean wilderness had been cabled far and wide. I have "died" so frequently since, that I am quite accustomed to it; it seems to be the best little thing I do.

The Museum was pleased with the results. I had explored and mapped a considerable area of unknown country and brought out a large collection of mammals and birds. Many of them were new to science. I felt that I had a sufficiently good excuse to wander for awhile and travel very slowly homeward.

CHAPTER XI

I TORE myself away from Seoul, Korea, with difficulty. It was a most attractive community. The life was absolutely free, a trifle wild at times but still had a strange tinge of formality as a left-over from the court days. The world was in front of me. Where should I go?

Peking first, of course. My previous visit to the city had given me a great desire to return as it does all visitors. The revolution of 1911 had just ended; the monarchy and the country were heaving with unrest, like a boiling caldron. Perhaps I could see a bit of looting and street fighting which would be interesting.

A little Japanese vessel from Chemulpho, Korea, took me to Port Arthur. There I went over the battlefields with a Japanese officer who had been through the siege. Two hundred three meter hill must have been a shambles. Probably in modern history there never was a more stubborn resistance or greater individual valor in attack than at that

KOREAN VILLAGERS.

An Old Peasant of Korea.

terrible spot. How quickly it would have been ended had the world then known the use of airplanes!

Peking was quiet to my disappointment, but a show started in Mukden and I took the first train for the north. Now, since I have lived in China, I realize that I was just one of those tourists whom the consuls hate. Seeking adventure and often finding serious trouble for themselves.

The affair in Mukden was ended when I arrived. It was the usual thing. Soldiers not paid; looting to collect what was due them and a bit more; street fighting for a day or two; executions! It is a story which has been repeated literally thousands of times in China since the life of the so-called republic. It was all new to me then.

I wished to see an execution! Such a morbid strain exists in everyone, I suppose. Usually one such spectacle is more than enough. It was in my case. Eighteen men lost their heads that day. Stripped to the waist, arms tightly bound behind their backs, they appeared quite indifferent to what was going on. They kneeled in a long line and the executioner went down the row lopping off heads like cabbages. I remember one fellow kept twisting about to see when his turn would come!

I won't describe the details. They were pretty awful and cured me from ever wishing to see another execution. I did not rid myself of the mental picture for weeks. I have seen many men killed since that time but never when I could avoid it. An execution is just about as attractive to me as a pest house.

I decided that I ought to go to Australia. I wasn't very keen about it but it was far away and I had not been in that part of the world. So I went to Shanghai and thence to Hongkong. In the club I met a man I knew. He was going across Siberia and wanted my company. "Can do" said I. Russia seemed more amusing than Australia, and I have always been glad that I saw it before the revolution.

In Moscow, we parted, he had to go to London, I eventually to Finland. A month in Sweden, Norway and Denmark and I sailed for New York. I had had no mail for weeks for I never could wait long enough for it to catch up to me and I had no plans. I was just wandering happily, drifting with the current of youthful desires until my money had disappeared.

The winter in New York passed in hard work. I wrote a monograph on the re-discovered California gray whale, offered it as a thesis at Columbia

University and took my degree in June. That was in 1913.

A few weeks later I went north on the yacht *Adventuress* belonging to John Borden of Chicago. It was to have been a sporting whale hunt but the vessel was delayed in getting around the Horn to San Francisco. We were too late to go into the ice and the trip became a shoot for caribou and bear along Alaskan shores.

But I did one job that was interesting and worth while. The Director of the U. S. Bureau of Fisheries had requested me to take motion pictures of the valuable fur seal herd in the Pribilof Islands in the Bering Sea. No one with a movie camera had been allowed on the islands. It was a real opportunity.

We dropped anchor off the rock bound coast of St. Paul's Island and a few days later the *Adventuress* sailed away leaving me with the hospitable government colony. Those two islands way out there in the Bering Sea have yielded much more than the entire purchase price of Alaska and all from the skins of the fur seals. I believe too that I am right in saying that they have been the subject of more debate and governmental literature than any other international question.

The seals, you must know, are divided into two distinct groups—fur seals and hair seals. The latter have comparatively little value commercially, but the former yield the rich soft fur which makes a seal skin coat worth hundreds of dollars. Perhaps thousands now—I haven't bought any lately!

All winter long the black rocks of the Pribilof's lie deserted, stark and cold. But in early spring come the old bull seals up from the south. Great hulking fellows they are, rolling in fat and filled with rutting wrath. Each one selects for himself a private station on the shore, destined to be the site of his prospective harem. The best locations are those nearest the water where the females will first come to land. But just because an old bull happens to get there first does not mean that he is left quietly in possession. Far from it. He has to defend his claim against all comers. Claim jumpers arrive in droves every hour. The choice sites for domestic establishments are soon gone and later arrivals either have to fight for what they want or take the back lots away from the beach. For days the shore is a roaring, bloody battlefield. Rearing on their hind flippers the bulls throw themselves at one another, slashing viciously with their long canine teeth, shoving, pounding, tearing. Perhaps the

original occupant is driven out. Then the new-
comer must hold his claim in daily battles. All this
is only preliminary to the real show. That begins
when the first soft-eyed female pokes her sleek head
out of the water in the white surf line.

"The girls are here. The girls are here," roar the
bulls. The beach seethes with excited swains. Modestly the little seal ladies swim toward the shore,
play coyly about in the surf, draw off to deeper water
tantalizing the impatient gentlemen bouncing up and
down on the rocks of their hard won homes.

When they finally decide to land, the fury
begins. Each bull rushes for the nearest female, trying to entice her to his home site. Pushing and shoving, fighting off other aspirants for the lady's flipper, he finally drives or beguiles her to his station.
Once there he has little time for love making for
other females are constantly arriving. The bull
seal believes in quantity rather than quality. He
never seems satisfied. His harem consists of from
five to sixty lady friends and they certainly keep
him busy. Each time he makes a dash to the water's
edge on another amorous excursion some neighbor
tries to steal a wife or two. Perhaps one of the girls
has been attracted by the beautiful curling mus-
tache or deep bass voice of a bull just a few yards

away. She gives him the high sign and makes a dash for freedom while friend husband's back is turned. She may gain a new home. More often she is unceremoniously hauled back and told not to try *that* again.

The rushing season ends when the females have all arrived. Then the beach is turned into a maternity ward. Almost every lady seal gives birth to a little black squalling baby within a week from the time she lands. As a matter of fact that is what she has come there for. The conceited bulls think it is the masculine charms that bring the females shoreward. They are dead wrong. It is only mother instinct. She wants her baby born in the old homestead where she herself first saw the light. She is a pretty good mother, too, is the lady seal. She doesn't believe in birth control. "One each year" is the seal motto and she does her duty conscientiously every spring.

But the old bull has a hard season. All through the summer he neither eats nor sleeps. It is just one long debauch of fighting and love making and guarding his harem against unscrupulous invaders. By September he is a wreck of his former self. All his fat has disappeared, for that is what he has been living on by absorption all summer. His bones protrude, his hide is torn and scarred, he is weary unto death. Blessed sleep is what he needs. Forsaking his harem, he waddles back into the long grass far away from the beach, there to stretch out in the warm sun. He will sleep for three weeks on end without waking if left undisturbed.

The little black babies are not having such an easy time of it during the summer. Many of them are crushed by their fighting fathers. They are always under foot and sometimes they wander a bit too far and lose their mothers. I often watched a hungry pup scramble up to a dozing female and settle down for a drink of milk. She would turn, sniff disgustedly at the youngster, and give him a smart slap with her flipper. None of that for her. She wasn't any public fountain. Her own baby needed all the milk she could furnish and she was not giving any away to stray gutter snipe.

I used to roar with laughter. I could just hear what she said as plainly as though she spoke my own language. If the baby was over persistent she would get really angry, cuff him hard and send him squalling away. Usually his own mother soon found him. I often saw a lady seal scrambling about, wild-eyed, exactly like any human mother.

"Where has Willie gone? I left him right here

when I went out to fish. Willie! Has any one seen
Willie?" Oh, it was so funny! And such cooing
and gurgling when the lost had been found! She
would gather the whimpering black pup to her breast
stretch out on the rocks and let him feed to his
stomach's content. The pups looked exactly alike
to me. All coal black with great, nearsighted eyes,
but every mother knew her own child right enough.
Doubtless it was by a distinctive odor rather than
by sight. The pups were courageous little things
and most awfully peppery. If I picked one up he
spat and swore like a trouper doing his best to bite
with his tiny needle-like teeth.

I never knew that seals had.to be taught to swim.
I thought they knew how to paddle instinctively like
a duck. Not at all. I used to watch the mothers
giving swimming lessons in the tide pools. The
babies were afraid of the water. They didn't want
to go in at all. Slaps and vigorous cuffing were required before they would even get their flippers wet.
Sometimes the mothers had to throw them bodily
into the pools. But once in they learned the motions
quickly enough.

Although the old bulls never left their harems,
the females and bachelors went out daily to fish.
Bachelors are those seals that have not yet reached

man's estate and the dignity of a harem. They are the one or two-year-old males, and theoretically are the only ones to kill for fur. The skin of an old bull is valueless. It is too thick and heavy and too scarred by fighting.

Unfortunately the female produces fur as fine as that of the bachelor. That is what has caused much of the international trouble. Pelagic sealing, *vis:* killing the animals out in the open sea, meant inevitable ruin to the seal herd. Russian, Japanese, British and American vessels hung about the islands beyond the three mile limit, and shot the animals when they were feeding. As many females as bachelors would be killed that way, and each dead mother meant a starving pup on land. It took years of diplomatic negotiations to end pelagic sealing. Then a closed season was put on the islands for five years. No seals at all were killed. When the herd had begun to increase the government killed and sold a certain number of bachelors annually.

Since every bull has a harem of from five to sixty females, and about equal numbers of both sexes are born each year, killing of a certain proportion of the surplus males was a positive benefit to the herd. It stopped undue fighting in which both females and young are frequently done to death. The old bulls do not intentionally kill their lady friends' off-spring, but in the heat of combat they can't watch carefully where they step. Sometimes they sit on the babies unavoidably.

Everything on the islands is now under government supervision. The number of unattached bachelors is accurately known and the proportion that should be killed is carefully estimated. When the time comes these are rounded up, driven slowly to the killing grounds and there mercifully knocked on the head. Each skin is tagged and sold at government auction.

Every skin must be plucked. The long coarse outer hair is pulled leaving only the soft under fur. This is brown and the skins must be dyed. The beautiful lustrous black could for many years only be obtained in London. I believe now that there are several places in America which have learned the dyeing process.

I used to lie behind the rocks watching the seals. Their eyesight is so poor that unless I showed myself against the skyline they never took alarm. When I walked boldly out on the beach there was a general and hurried exodus to the water. There they would bob about in the surf like so many black corks, until I had retired from sight. In half an

There are Some Quiet Corners in Japan.

These Circular Doorways Contribute to the Beauty of Chinese Courtyards.

hour they were back again on the "rookeries" taking up the duties of family life.

I arrived at one beach where there were six thousand seals when a terrific gale was blowing. The surf pounded in tremendous breakers upon the rocks. For hours I lay concealed "shooting" bits of intimate seal life with the movie camera. Then I walked out upon the shore line. Like a church congregation standing to sing, the six thousand seals rose as one. For a few moments they gazed at me and then broke for the beach. They poured over each other in a living flood down the rocks and into the water. Riding the breakers like surf boats they floated in the waves and out again while I ground off hundreds of feet of film. What a picture that was! I might have remained all summer without another like it.

Guards along the shore always were on watch for poachers. A vessel might sneak up to one of the rookeries during a gale or at night and kill hundreds of seals before they were discovered. The value of the skins was worth the risk. Therefore, at every beach there were armories and small cannon. It was the only way to protect the herd. Soft words and courteous phrases did not carry weight with the wild seal poachers. But bullets they could understand. Kipling has told of one such fight in that wonderful poem, "The Rhyme of the Three Sealers." But I believe that in recent years there has been little poaching. The revenue cutters are too active during the summer months and in the winter the Bering Sea is an ice filled waste.

Then the government residents are isolated from the outside world. They have the radio, of course, but no aid could reach them. The cemetery on the hill slope tells its own sad story of those wanderers who have died a lonely death on the cheerless wastes of this bleak island.

I found my old friend Fred Chamberlin of the *Albatross* recently installed on St. Paul's as government naturalist. He was sick unto death with tuberculosis. Never should he have gone to that fog-bound coast. Long before the winter's end he would have joined the little colony in the white fenced cemetery. I sent a report by radio to Washington and we caught the last revenue cutter of the season to take him out.

The government introduced blue foxes on the islands. They were bred for fur and did very well. One fox used to come in every morning to the cook house at the time a little dog got his breakfast. The fox would annoy the dog and entice him away from his food, then rush back like a streak of blue lightning, grab a bone and vanish. After a few losses of this kind, the dog learned his lesson. One day he was exasperated beyond endurance, he dashed wildly after his tormentor, but carried the bone with him. Who says that animals don't think?

There was a herd of reindeer on St. Paul's. It was one of the first attempts to introduce the animals into Alaska for commercial breeding. Now the industry is well founded.

The seals, foxes and reindeer gave me a harvest of pictures and the government authorities were delighted.

On the way back to Seattle the *Adventuress* stopped at Prince Rupert. Just five years ago I had seen the beginning of the town. Then there was a long wharf, a winding broad sidewalk and a few shacks for the engineers in a wide clearing of the forest. Nothing else. When we stepped off the yacht that October day in 1913 an automobile was waiting. It carried us over wide paved streets and past great modern buildings to a luxurious club. All this in five years. I could hardly believe my eyes.

The winter of 1913–14 found me in the Museum writing a monograph on the sei whale. In October

I was married to Yvette Borup, sister of another explorer, George Borup, who was with Admiral Peary on his successful North Pole expedition. The next summer we spent in the Adirondack woods taking moving pictures of deer and collecting a summer group for the Museum. It was great fun.

Plans were already forming in my mind for a complete change of work. Whales were well enough but the subject was too limited. I could spend my entire life studying whales but I did not want to specialize to that extent. Already I had made unique collections for the Museum, enough to fill an enormous hall. I had written two extensive monographs and many shorter scientific papers on the subject. I felt that I had done my duty by the whales.

CHAPTER XII

LAND exploration was in my mind. Ever since the Korean expedition of 1912 I had been sure that that was what I could do best and what would make me happiest. The lure of new lands, the thrill of the unknown, the desire to know what lay over the next hill! Central Asia was the magnet which drew me irresistibly. Professor Osborn's prophecy that it would prove to be the incubating center for northern mammalian life was a seed which had fallen on fertile ground in my brain. I determined some day to test that theory. It seemed to me that in Central Asia lay the real opportunity for scientific exploration.

But Central Asia is a grim place. It could not be entered casually and I was not ready to do it yet. I wanted first to nibble at the edges of the great plateau; to learn the languages, customs and physical problems of the surrounding regions; to fit myself thoroughly to do the job.

I proposed to the President of the Museum a series of expeditions for work in Asia extending over a period of ten years. The first was to be strictly zoölogical. The main work to lie in Yun-nan Province, China, and along the Tibetan frontier. It was a little known region geographically, as well as scientifically.

He agreed enthusiastically as usual, but financing it was something of a problem. It would only cost fifteen thousand dollars, but the Museum did not have that much to spend. I told them that I would guarantee to raise half the amount among my personal friends if the Museum would do the other half. It was not so easy, but eventually I got the money.

We left early in March, 1916, went first to Peking and then to Foochow via Shanghai. Our objective was to join a shooting missionary, Harry Caldwell, who had made quite a reputation for himself in China. With a Bible in one hand and a rifle in the other he pursued his evangelical work among the Chinese, ridding their villages of man-eating tigers, the while he poured into their ears the Eternal Truth. Harry is a regular fellow. Bursting with enthusiasm, interested in everything under the sun but particularly in natural history, he has done much real good among the people of his district.

Some years earlier he had discovered a "blue"

tiger. Twice he had seen it at close range and the natives knew it well. The beast had become a man-eater, and was credited with many victims. I wished to kill it. Caldwell described it as striped with black on a blue-gray ground. Doubtless it was a partially melanistic phase of the ordinary yellow tiger. Melanism, the opposite of albinism, occurs very frequently in some animals but is rare in others. Black leopards are common but no dark colored tigers had been previously reported.

The animal ranged in a district about Futsing not far from Foochow. It was the same method of hunting I had had in Korea. Hard traveling from village to village whenever the beast was reported by the natives. The heat was terrible. Wet, soggy air, blazing sun, fast traveling, hard climbing. Once we missed the tiger by a hair's breadth. Natives had seen it go into a deep ravine filled with an impenetrable jungle of swordgrass and thorn bushes. Caldwell and I staked out another goat with her kid in a small clearing. We concealed ourselves in the grass on a hillside thirty feet away. The kid kept up a continual bawling. This was what we relied upon to entice the animal from its lair just before sundown. Caldwell had killed seven tigers that way.

For two hours we waited watching the shadows creep further up the hillslopes. Velvety blackness lay thick in the deeper recesses of the ravine. There came the faintest sound of a rolling pebble; then another. Caldwell put his mouth close to my ear and whispered: "Get ready. He's coming."

The tiger was there, not twenty feet from us, taking a last survey before he dashed into the open to leap upon the goat. I sat waiting, every nerve tense; the butt of my rifle nestled against my cheek.

Suddenly pandemonium broke loose. Over the hill opposite to us came a party of wood cutters. Blowing horses and banging tin pans, they streamed down the slope across the bottom of the ravine and up the other side. They were taking a short cut home, and the noise was to protect them from a tiger's attack. Our chance was gone.

In spite of the fact that my companion was a missionary I did some really artistic cursing. Had those confounded Chinese arrived ten minutes later the tiger would have been lying dead in front of us. Instead he had quietly withdrawn into the depths of his lair. We found the pug marks where the great beast had crouched right at the edge of the long grass. It was rotten luck but the old men of the village wagged their heads and said:

Two Young Chinese of the Yung-Chang Province.

AN UNWILLING PASSENGER: FERRYING MULES IN NORTH CHINA.

"You can never kill him. He is not a proper tiger. It is an evil spirit." All of them believed it too. For a month we hunted him, time after time almost getting a shot. It did seem that the beast was a phantom; that it was possessed of some occult power to evade the waiting death.

After we left, Caldwell had another go at the blue tiger, but never even saw him. Others have hunted him since, but he is still at large. His death-list now reaches nearly a hundred people according to the natives. Later reports said that another had appeared and that the two hunted together. It may be so.

While we were in the tiger country Edmund Heller joined us for the trip to Yunnan and we went by ship to Haiphong, Indo-China, thence up the picturesque French railway to Yunnan-fu. With a caravan of thirty-five ponies, we started westward for Tali-fu, right in the center of the province.

We had been warned of bandits and at the end of every march were given a guard of four or five soldiers. We did not want the wretched fellows but were required to take them. Usually they carried an extraordinary assortment of ancient firearms and few of the cartridges would fit their rifles. We felt sure that they would be the first to run if brigands were encountered. They did not disappoint us. Nine days out just as we were climbing a rocky pass to the summit of a ten-thousand-foot mountain, a breathless Chinese came tearing down the road. He was too excited to talk coherently but I caught the word *tu-fei* (brigand) several times. A moment later our soldiers were breaking all speed records on the back trail!

I soon discovered that a caravan had been attacked less than half a mile in front of us. The bandits were even then going through the goods. We were in a bad place for a fight but I got our party to the summit of the hill and arranged a barricade with the loads. Then we did a little scouting. From a high rock we could see the brigands right below us ripping open the packages and scattering their contents right and left. There were forty of them. I could have easily killed half a dozen but decided to let them alone if they did not molest us.

They found what they were after, several packages of jade, and disappeared into the mountains. We learned that they had been following this caravan for several days. It belonged to a rich mandarin and the bandits knew just what he had among his possessions.

At Tali-fu with a new caravan we started for the Snow Mountain near the Tibetan frontier. It proved to be a wonderful collecting ground. Virgin forest extended almost up to the snow line at fourteen thousand feet. We got serow and goral, strange goat-like animals inhabitants only of Asia, and dozens of new species of squirrels, shrews, voles, rats and mice. We were camped at 12,000 feet in a beautiful open meadow with snow-covered peaks almost encircling us. Cloud masses dipped and swirled about the tents but with a charcoal fire in an open brazier we were snug and warm.

Here I contracted a severe infection in the palm of my right hand and we had to move to a little temple at the base of the mountain. I should have died except for the devoted nursing of my wife. Day by day she watched the infection spread and saw my arm swell almost to bursting. At night I was delirious. Steaming cloths changed every few minutes all through the night and day eventually controlled the poison. Still it was weeks before I could use my hand again.

We had a difficult time in crossing a pass 16,000 feet high into the Yangtze drainage region. In a few hours we came from the warm sun of October to the dead of winter. Up through a larch forest, into the higher belt of dwarf bamboo beyond the uttermost timber line of rhododendrons we climbed. The summit of the pass was bare and bleak, frozen hard. A bitter wind swirled about our tent. It was too cold to sleep. All night we shivered about a tiny fire for we could find little wood. Three of the ponies died from cold and the effects of the altitude. Most of the men suffered severely but all were game. It was a miserable party that descended next morning into the golden sunshine of mid-October.

Every mountain range which we crossed brought us into new valleys occupied by strange aboriginal people. There are thirty distinct tribes in Yunnan, the remnants of the original inhabitants of China. Just as the white men pushed the American Indians westward so did the Chinese drive the aborigines south and west unknown centuries ago. Now they have concentrated in the wild mountains of Yunnan. One of them, the Lolos, never have been subdued by the Chinese. They still occupy a territory called "Lolo land" in the midst of Szechwan, one of the richest provinces of China. No Chinese is allowed in Lolo land. Instant death is the penalty. Small bands of Lolos have wandered from the forbidden country and settled in Yunnan.

After crossing the mountain pass we descended to a Lolo village hidden away deep in a secluded valley. Fine tall fellows they were, with long heads, high bridged noses, and thin lips; almost a Caucasian type of face. They never had seen a white person and at first were frightened. Cigarettes and small presents soon made them realize that we were friends. Of course everything about us was interesting. Cameras, watches and the like were too far beyond their comprehension to be impressive, but field glasses seemed a miracle. My high-power rifle and automatic pistol were tools of a god. From them I purchased a sheep for demonstration. I showed them the tiny 6.5 mm. Mannlicher bullet and tied the sheep 200 yards away on the hillside. The whole village was breathless with suspense when I fired and the animal fell, they brought it back with wonder and awe in their faces. Their own guns were primitive matchlock things having a range of thirty yards.

In photographs they could not recognize themselves for they never had seen their own faces. It was only by pointing to some special article of dress and then indicating it in the photograph that they could be made to understand. In my wife's mirror they saw themselves for the first time. The Lolo women would have sold their souls to possess it.

Passing through the Moso country, up to the frontier of Tibet we went, finding new mammals and birds, new plants, new tribes and unmapped trails. The Tibetans were shy of the camera. It was only by subterfuge that my wife could get a photograph. One day we concealed ourselves beside a trail with the movie camera behind a bush. Along came a party of Tibetans, men and women, single file. When in just the right position we pulled down the bush and began to crank the camera. Each man grabbed a woman holding her struggling body in front of him. They were taking no chances with their precious selves. Tin cans and bottles were our best currency. Money meant little, for they had no way to spend it. Tea, knives and almost any trinket could be exchanged for chickens, eggs or sheep.

We pushed across the Yangtze River where it rushes out of a black canyon, its depths unknown to any human being, and into the gorge of the Mekong. In late January back to Tali-fu. A fortnight there to rest and engage a new caravan, then southward toward the Burma border.

Days upon days of steady traveling before we dropped down into the valley of the Nam-ting River and the humid heat of the tropics. Nowhere could we have found a greater contrast. Thick palm jungle instead of snow-capped peaks; leopard, sambur, and monkeys; peacocks and half a dozen other pheasants.

The first morning I was up at daylight to solve a mystery. From a score of places in the jungle came the "cock-a-do-dle-do" of barnyard roosters. The last note was a little short but otherwise exactly the same. We were a long way from any domestic fowls. What did it mean? Cautiously I stalked the sounds. Startled clucking came from a thick tree in front; suddenly into a burst of flaming red and gold five birds sailed into the open. I fired quickly and then again. Two were down. In another moment I had solved the mystery. They were jungle fowl! Stupid of me not to have suspected it. Centuries before Christ these birds had been domesticated and from them come all the breeds of our barnyard fowls. I had killed two beautiful roosters in full spring plumage; they looked exactly like diminutive game cocks.

Every morning and evening sweet mournful calls sounded in the jungle. We knew that they were monkeys but stalking was difficult, for from the upper branches they could look down into the thick jungle and see us easily. But we learned how to do it finally and got a dozen specimens. They were gibbons—one of the anthropoid or "man-like" apes —of a rare species.

From the Nam-ting River we traveled north skirting the Burma border. We could not go across because we had no permits to shoot and the World War was on. But we lost ourselves and had to cross the frontier to the little village of Ma-li-pa to find out where we were. There we were taken prisoner by a delightful English officer, Captain Clive, who was fretting his heart out on frontier duty while his regiment was active in Africa. But "someone must do it" said the army chief and he happened to be that "someone."

From him we got our first news in many months. America had joined the Allies and we were in the war! Half around the world from the battlefields of France, in the midst of a Burmese jungle, still that word somehow took all the joy out of life for me. I wanted to go back to do my bit whatever it was to be. We had long since determined to come out by

The Ancient Sport of Falconry: Boy with Hunting Hawk in North China.

A Woman of the Liso Tribe: North China.

way of Bhamo and Rangoon on the Irawadi River. We would go there now as fast as possible. Fortunately we were near the end of our planned exploration and the traverse could be completed in a few more weeks.

Captain Clive was in touch with Rangoon by heliograph and in five days came permission for us to depart in peace by any route we chose. I wanted much to have a look at the terrible Salween Valley which lay between us and Bhamo. A ghastly place it is, hot, dry, deserted of all human life, given over to peacocks, leopards and wild red dogs. Even the aboriginal natives, Lisos, dare not face the malignant malaria which makes of the valley a fever stricken hell. Only deep injections of quinine will kill those germs. Without them one dies. In a week, I thought, we should be able to get a good representation of the fauna and with extraordinary precautions escape the fever.

The place was fascinating even though we knew that we were flirting with death to remain at all. Our reward was a fine collection. Almost all the mammals, I believe, were new to science. No one else had cared to go there. Whenever I fired a gun it was answered from a dozen places in the jungle by the mournful wail of peacocks. *Meaow, meaow,*

meaow! How to get them? Stalking was impossible for the dry leaves crackled like chips under our feet. We learned that the birds came down to drink every evening at sand pits on the opposite shore. Lying in wait brought us several gorgeous specimens. One evening Heller, who was watching a point a hundred yards up stream, saw an old peacock out-wit me. I had heard a scratching in the jungle and had turned my back to the water expecting every moment to see a peacock strut out from cover. Meantime a splendid male had walked along the beach and was quietly drinking within twenty feet of where I crouched. Heller saw the bird jump upon a stone and catch sight of me; then, flattened almost to the ground, slip back into the thick cover. I would have known nothing of the little drama had Heller not seen it all.

A single attack of fever which laid me flat for a few days was our only ill effect from the Salween Valley. A week of hunting the black gibbons of Ho-mu-shu on a steep mountain spine, and we made our way to Teng-yueh, one of the outposts of civilization. It is a customs station on the main trade route from Burma to China. There is a British Consul, half a dozen missionaries and several foreign members of the customs staff. Not a bad place to live, Teng-yueh. A fine climate, comfortable houses and splendid schooling.

Mail was awaiting us there, the first in many months. Ten days later we came into Bhamo, called on the commissioner and were invited to use the Circuit House, a glorified *dak* bungalow. He took us to the club that night. How strange and shy we felt. To see women in filmy dresses sipping cold drinks on the lawn; to hear a band and converse with officers in spotless uniforms!

For nine months we had been in the wilderness of China's hinterland, away from others of our kind, but neither of us could say good-bye to the mountains and the jungle without regret.

To get our collections back to New York through a war-mad world was more difficult than to gather them in the field. Every port of shipping space was taken for months in advance on every freighter. Only by prayers and pull and personal persuasion did I get them to Calcutta, across India to Bombay and then back again to Hongkong. It was a long way around but I could not choose. I chaperoned those boxes every mile. When I saw them piled safely in the American Museum of Natural History I felt that had been the most difficult job that I would ever have to do.

CHAPTER XIII

I SHALL have to omit a record of that part of my life from the time that I returned to America in 1917 to the end of the war. I may say that I was not in jail; also that I did much wandering. The winter of 1918–19 found me in Peking. My wife and our year old baby were also there, established in our first Oriental home.

Now that the war was ended I had an intense desire to return at once to my interrupted plans for Central Asian exploration. Our expedition to Yunnan and the Tibetan frontier had left me with some very definite thoughts on the subject of future work.

We had been in one of the most interesting regions of the world from the standpoint of general science. It had been difficult and dangerous to get there. Expensive as well. What were our results? The largest and most complete collection of mammals that had ever been taken from a single region of Asia. Also many birds and some reptiles and fish.

It was all that we had proposed to do and the Museum authorities were delighted.

Still I had a most uncomfortable feeling of opportunities missed. What of the many aboriginal tribes we had seen? Tribes which represented the very earliest inhabitants of China and which were rapidly disappearing. I was convinced that among those primitive people, some of whom are living virtually in the Stone Age in those somber mountain valleys, lay the answer to many questions which were puzzling the students of Asiatic anthropology.

What of the geology of this vast region? Almost nothing was known of it, yet it was of great importance in the study of continent building.

What of the past animal life and its relation to the rest of the world? A blank space—utterly blank!

What of the archæology, the record of those early Stone Age peoples who must have lived in and passed through this country? Not a thing was known.

So the story went through every branch of science. Great opportunities missed because I was not a zoologist, anthropologist, archæologist, palæontologist and geologist all combined in one individual. But even had I had expert knowledge in all these branches what could I have done? Very little, for each study would have required every moment of one man's time.

Again, how my own work was hampered because I did not have an intimate knowledge of several other sciences. So many puzzling zoological problems could have been clarified if I had been an expert botanist or geologist! It had given me sufficient food for thought.

Obviously there was only one solution of such a situation. On the great expedition to Central Asia which was always in the back of my mind I must take representatives of every branch of science involved in our main problems. Then, in the field, we would have the benefit of full discussion by experts of every question which arose. That was the only possible method by which to attack Central Asia; if we were to do anything less, the work would be only superficial.

Peking was the gateway to Mongolia, a part of Central Asia. Also a part which I knew somewhat, for I had crossed it several times during the past year. I would give it a more careful study and see if it warranted the first invasion by the expedition of my dreams.

The Museum authorities were agreeable for it would not require much money. The expedition was

to consist only of my wife and myself with three or
four natives as assistants. While we should collect
mammals and birds it was designed chiefly as a
reconnaissance for future work.

Motor cars ran infrequently between Kalgan,
124 miles from Peking, and Urga, the capital of
Mongolia. I arranged with Charles Coltman to
take us to Urga. Our equipment went by camel
three months in advance. I had made several trips
with Coltman but we little knew that this was the
last time we should ever travel the desert trails together. Three years later he was brutally murdered
by Chinese soldiers just beyond the gates of Kalgan!

Never again will I have such a feeling as Mongolia gave me. The broad sweeps of dun gravel merg-
ing into a vague horizon; the ancient trails once
travelled by Genghiz Khan's wild raiders; the violent contrast of motor cars beside majestic camels
fresh from the marching sands of the western Gobi!
All this thrilled me to the core. I had found my
country. The one I had been born to know and love.
Somewhere in the depths of that vast, silent desert
lay those records of the past that I had come to
seek.

We had two cars. One of them carried Mr. and

Mrs. Ted MacCallie, who were to manage Coltman's trading station in Urga; we occupied the other. It was to be a leisurely trip with stops to shoot antelope and wolves along the way. We had lots of fun with the gazelle. Nothing on four legs can equal them in speed. Like all plains animals they cannot resist a motor car. It was a fatal fascination which draws them like a magnet from hundreds of yards on either side. They just have to cross in front of it or their lives are ruined.

At first a gazelle will lope along at twenty or twenty-five miles an hour, head up, sometimes leaping into the air as though on springs drawing always closer to the car. Then with a sudden rush he tries to cross in front. He goes just fast enough to keep well away from the motor. One might think he was running at full speed. But just drop a bullet near him and see what happens. He seems to flatten out, his legs are only a blur like the wings of an electric fan, and he really begins to run. After many tests we have put the maximum speed for the first dash at sixty miles an hour. This is a conservative estimate. He cannot maintain a mile-a-minute pace for more than half a mile; then he drops to forty miles an hour at which he can continue for a long distance.

Once while we were following a herd of gazelle

we ran over a sharp rise and down the long slope of a wide valley. A wolf, lying asleep behind a rock, suddenly leaped out in front of us. There were a dozen antelope on either side but he was not interested. Neither were they. Then a fat yellow marmot joined the procession, rushed along for a few yards and frantically ducked underground. We seemed to be driving a whole zoological garden. Coltman stepped on the gas but a sand-spit intervened and the fleeing menagerie scattered to the four winds of heaven.

There was a portable Delco electric light plant, destined for the Living Buddha of Urga, packed in the back of MacCallie's car. One of our camps was near a Mongol village. That night Mac rigged a great arclight on a pole for we wanted to give the Mongols a real celebration. To our surprise not one came near us. Next morning when we stepped out of the tent, the village was gone. I rubbed my eyes and looked again. It had been there last night right enough; a dozen *yurts* and perhaps five hundred sheep. Now the place was bare. The Mongols had been so frightened by the strange ball of light suddenly appearing in the desert that they had packed their yurts and left with every man, woman and sheep!

Superstition is a Mongol's middle name. Anything that he does not understand is attributed to some supernatural agency. By this means the lamas (priests) keep their power over the laymen.

Sometimes this superstition becomes most annoying. Last year, in a part of the desert where we were working, there had been no rain for some time. Shortly after we left, torrential downpours swept away half a dozen yurts pitched at the bottom of a steep bluff. The priests had to have an alibi for such a calamity. We were it. Because those foreigners dug bones there, said they, the Gods are angry and produced the floods!

Again rinder-pest had taken a dreadful toll of cattle near one of our fossil deposits. The lamas blamed it all on us. They refused to let us continue work there. But I persuaded the high priest to visit our camp. After three drinks of brandy I showed him twenty-five dollars and asked if he didn't think the Gods could be appeased. He pocketed the money and agreed that it might be done. But he particularly stated that it must be a secret between us two. The Gods would be annoyed, said he, if I mentioned it to any of the other lamas!

Urga, the city of the Living Buddha, is one of the most interesting places I have ever seen. Colt-

AN ANCIENT GATEWAY AND STREET IN YUN-NAN.

CURIOUS TEMPLE IN YUN-NAN.

man left us there to return to Kalgan. At that time (1919) it was as free as air. We could come and go without restriction as though we were on the open plains. Today, it is a far different place. Since the Russian Soviet took Outer Mongolia under their "protection" Urga has become a city of suspicion. It is difficult enough to enter, Heaven knows, but to get out is even worse. Every person, stranger or resident, is a potential spy and is watched accordingly.

Both my wife and I were fascinated with the bizarre, medieval life of Urga. It was like a pageant on the stage of the Hippodrome. When a dozen wild nomads in flaming red, yellow or purple dashed at full speed down the main street it seemed that we must be present at some special celebration; that this barbaric spectacle could not be the life of every day.

At that time Urga numbered about twenty-five thousand inhabitants but fully fifteen thousand were lamas. The Living Buddha, who ranked only after the Dalai and Tashi Lamas of Tibet, was the actual head of both church and state. Now he is dead and I saw his mummified body in a very sacred temple which I had entered by a ruse. Then he was old and blind but he had been a gay bird in his day. The stories of his revels with a few chosen spirits were the talk of Urga.

I visited him in his palace beside the Tola River. An amazing place it was, filled with western inventions gleaned from mail order catalogues of America. The Living Buddha ordered a motor car to be brought from Peking. He seldom rode in it but had much amusement by attaching a wire to the batteries and giving worshipping pilgrims an electric shock. They thought that they had been especially blessed by the Living God!

My wife and I pitched our tent on a beautiful green lawn beside the river. It would have been a charming spot except for the dogs which swarmed like ants about the city. Thousands of them maintained a continual roar around us all through the night and day. Huge black mastiffs they were, savage as wolves and always starving. It was worth one's life to pass through the meat market at night. We never ventured away from camp without a club or pistol.

The Mongols do not bury their dead but throw them out to be devoured by the dogs, wolves and birds. Almost every day some corpse was dragged down by the river from the lama city. One was left within a hundred yards of our tent. It took just seven minutes for a pack of dogs to tear it into a dozen pieces. It was not a nice sight.

My wife nearly met a horrible death from these same dogs when returning from Mongolia. We were camped for the night at Turin, a great mass of jagged rocks not far from a desert monastery. It was a starlight night and we did not bother to pitch a tent. Our sleeping bags were spread side by side near the car. I had placed two rifles between us on the ground. One was my 6.5 mm. Mannlicher; the other a tiny .22 cal. repeater I had used for killing birds. The usual chorus of barking dogs sounded faintly from the monastery but I thought nothing of it. During the night my wife was restless and at two o'clock sat up suddenly, wide awake. In the moonlight she saw a pack of fourteen huge dogs stealthily circling about our camp. As they closed in she screamed. Half awake, I grasped the first rifle my hands touched and fired blindly. It happened to be the .22 Winchester. The tiny bullet caught the huge leader in some vital spot for he sank in his tracks stone dead. As the pack swept by I fired twice more hitting two other dogs. Instantly there was a blood curdling chorus of yelps, and growls as the wounded animals were devoured by their ravenous comrades.

I 'never knew where the bullet struck the leader. I dragged him far beyond our camp and the next morning all that remained of his carcass were a few bits of bloody hair. Had my wife not waked at that very second we would never have lived to see another day.

Every family and every caravan owns a dog. They are encouraged to be savage. God help the person that comes near a Mongol *yurt* unannounced. Often a particularly vicious dog is kept in a wooden cage and only allowed free at night to range the compound.

I have had six or eight very narrow escapes from being killed by dogs during my ten years in Mongolia. One night as I rode into Urga on horseback four dogs attacked me. One leaped for my stirrup leather, another for the pony's tail and a third caught him by the fetlock. As I reached to draw my rifle from the scabbard the pony kicked wildly rolling over one of the hounds. Instantly the others were on their injured companion tearing him to bits.

From Urga my wife and I went southward into the grasslands. Our equipment was carried in three carts; we, ourselves, rode ponies. For weeks we camped from place to place trapping small mammals, collecting birds and antelope.

Shooting gazelle from motor cars is butchery. Hunting them on horseback is sport. We would ride over the plains scanning the country from every rise, until antelope were sighted. Then ride quietly toward them, gradually edging nearer until they began to run. Almost always they would try to cross in front. With a yell I would be off at full speed, standing in the stirrups, rifle free. Jumping ditches, among treacherous marmot holes, down into valleys and out again, wild with excitement. Then suddenly checking the pony I would throw myself off and begin to shoot. That was real sport. The marmot holes made it exceedingly dangerous and the antelope had much the advantage. They could run twice as fast as the best pony. All I had was a high power rifle.

My pony Kublai Khan loved the sport. He was just like a shooting dog. Often he would see gazelle before we did and would toss his head restlessly, wild to be off. I could shoot from the saddle or right under his nose while he stood quietly. When we came up to the dead antelope, he would nozzle it proudly as though he had done it all himself.

It is not easy at first to shoot a gazelle going fifty to sixty miles an hour at three hundreds yards. But it comes with practice. Suddenly you will get the knack, learn just how much to lead the animals and the rest is easy. For the first fortnight I averaged one antelope to ten cartridges. By the end of the season I had cut it down to one in two.

My wife and I lived much on game. Sand grouse and bustard varied the diet of antelope; sometimes we could buy a sheep from the nomad Mongols. It was a free healthy life and we were happy. I was learning the country and its ways, talking with wandering Mongols about the far western desert, studying the physical problems of transport and maintenance in the arid reaches of the Gobi. All I learned made me more certain that this was the chosen spot for the new conquest of Central Asia; the place where I could stake all to lose or win on a single play.

We were seldom far from the main Kalgan-Urga trail in the northern grasslands. With our carts and ponies it would have been impossible to go into the desert. There was neither enough feed nor water. Camels alone could be used there. But that made little difference for we were gathering a superb collection of mammals and I was getting the "feel of the country."

CHAPTER XIV

EARLY in July of that year we wandered back to Urga and from there went north into the great larch forests. In less than twenty miles from the city we were out of the plains fauna into the Siberian life zone. A wilderness of virgin forest swept over the mountains inhabited only by moose, elk, roedeer, bear, wild boar and lynx. Capercaille, black grouse, hazel hens and ptarmigan were abundant in almost every parklike opening of the forest. In contrast to what we had left, it might have been another world.

Far up in the wilderness, in a secluded river valley, we found a Mongol village and a strange old hunter. Tserin Dorchy was his name. I bore a message to him from a Mongol duke, but that would have made precious little difference had he not liked us. Of all human beings I have ever met he was the most independent. His word was law in the village. But our mutual love for sport soon put us on a friendly basis and we were accepted as welcome additions to the valley's community.

Our main camp was a mile above the village and always some of the Mongols were at the tents.

Immediately I had to assume my usual rôle of doctor. All sorts of diseases were brought to me for treatment. Tserin Dorchy's wife presented a baby with a case of eczema and before the month was out I had the kiddie well on the road to health. A wandering lama had ridden into the village shortly before our arrival. He had been saying prayers for all the community invalids but none of them were better for it. When my treatments began to have beneficial affects, he stole all my glory. I think most of the Mongols were convinced that the foreign medicines really did the work but they were too superstitious to admit the fact openly. Anyway, whenever one of my patients showed signs of recovery the lama collected a fee. He was a rich man as lamas go, in the way of sheep, boots and clothing before we left the valley. He never offered to split fifty-fifty with me either. But you couldn't have dragged him away as long as we remained.

He settled himself comfortably in the village. A preëmptory demand got him the finest *yurt* that the community boasted. Then he looked over the feminine members and selected one of Tserin Dorchy's eighteen year old daughters to share his temporary prosperity. I don't think she liked it much for she was enamoured of one of my Chinese assistants, but disinclination did not get her anywhere. Even the independent old Tserin Dorchy was too superstitious to offend the lama. He was afraid of the curses which the priestly visitor might place upon him and all his flocks. Still the lama did not seem to mind greatly when his temporary wife rode out at night to keep a tryst in the moonlight with my taxidermist!

Chastity is hardly a virtue in a Mongol's scheme of life. It isn't considered important. The Mongols are simply immoral according to Western standards. They have definite marriage customs, of course, and I think that few of them have more than one wife, but that is merely a matter of economics. A harem would be too expensive either to acquire or maintain.

The lamas are forbidden to marry but I have known only one or two who took their vows seriously enough to let them interfere with the pleasures of feminine society. As a result of such promiscuity considerably more than half the entire population of the country is infected with devasting diseases. Naturally such a condition plays havoc with healthy offspring and the race is rapidly disappearing. Those children that do live are as hard as nails. Certainly they are the survival of the fittest if there ever was such a thing. The poor kiddies simply don't have a chance. Filth surrounds them from the day they are born. The ordinary *yurt* is not only a stable for young sheep, goats and calves but a playground for the babies. Unsanitary isn't the word. As Mark Twain said about the Ganges River:

"It is so filthy that germs can't live in it."

An ordinary Mongol never takes a bath from the time he is born until he dies unless it be by accident. There are certain extenuating circumstances for water is scarce and during most of the year the bitter cold makes bathing disagreeable. Also about as soon as one is clean a sand storm nullifies all the good work. I must confess that I myself once went for nearly a month without a bath during a period of continual sand storms. The effort just did not seem worth while, with a temperature below freezing and a yellow haze filling the tent.

One thing saves the lives of many Mongols and that is sunlight. They live out of doors most of the day and the thin population, even in the grasslands, breeds few germs. When the interior of a

A Stop for Luncheon in Yun-nan.

OUR CAMP AT THE BLACK AND WHITE WATER: YUN-NAN.

yurt becomes too dirty even for them, they simply shift it a few yards to another spot.

This for the summer. Winter is the time when trouble comes. Then it is too cold to stay outside and usually a wall of dung is constructed about the *yurt* to act not only as a store of fuel but as a wind break. The house is seldom shifted in the winter. The children become incredibly hardy. I have seen three or four year old babies stark naked playing about in a bitter wind when I was shivering in a fur coat. The kiddies are taught to ride when they are hardly able to walk. Often they are tied on horseback. If by chance they fall off such an accident evokes no sympathy. At five or six years they are herding sheep or camels and doing it amazingly well.

I believe that the present day Mongol is equal in endurance or very nearly so to those of Genghiz Khan's time. The weak have not survived. Of course there are not as many of them but the hardship and privation which they can endure upon occasion is little short of superhuman.

With all their faults they are distinctly a likeable people. Good sportsmen, ready to try anything once, brave, strong, self reliant, excellent fighters, magnificent horsemen. They possess so many of the characteristics which Anglo-Saxons admire that we have many points of contact. Most of all, the Mongols have a sense of humor. They are able even to appreciate a joke upon themselves which is more than many of our own people can boast.

Independence is perhaps their most distinctive characteristic. Their way of life upon the plains has made them supremely self reliant and to acknowledge a master, either individually or as a nation, is abhorrent. Witness the political changes of the last two decades when they have become affiliated first with China, then with Russia and back again. Each change was brought about because the greater power had become intolerably domineering. They hoped that by switching to the other neighbor, relief might come.

I was continually impressed by the similarity in the customs of Mongolia and those of our own great west during the early days. Like conditions bred like habits. Hospitality is a law of the land. Time after time I have ridden up to a *yurt,* hobbled my pony and gone inside. A place about the fire was made for me as a matter of course. Taking out my little wooden food bowl I dipped into the common pot and was given tea. Always they spread my blankets in the best sleeping place farthest from the door.

In the morning there was no thought of payment. I have done the same thing for dozens of Mongols at my own camp.

Our ponies often slipped their hobbles and strayed during the night. Many times they were brought back by natives who had found them miles away. They would expect as much from us. It is a law of the land to inform every traveller if a well or spring is dry. To be caught without water may mean death.

Horse stealing is as great a crime as murder. Death is the only punishment. The few Mongol soldiers in Urga were kept to enforce such laws. If a man reported the theft of a pony the soldiers took up the trail following it for days or weeks if need be and seldom returned without their man.

In those days (1919) the Mongols were still using one of the most horrible forms of punishment of which I know. A prisoner was placed in a heavy wooden coffin about four and one half feet long by three feet wide and as many high. He could neither lie down nor sit erect. In this cramped position he might stay for days or weeks or even years according to his sentence. Through a round hole six inches wide in the side of the box food was passed—when the jailers did not forget it! In the prison I saw a dozen coffins and all were occupied.

One of the inmates told me that he had been there five years; his was a life sentence. At first he used to be taken out every week for a little exercise but soon his legs and arms had atrophied and he could no longer walk. Still he lived. Many coffins on the street corners contained men who had committed minor crimes. They would remain inside for perhaps a week or two and could be given food by any one who wished. I saw one poor fellow in a box whose legs and hands were tightly manacled as well. Fortunately this punishment was abolished in 1920. The last time I visited the jail in Urga I saw a pile of old coffins in a corner of the yard and none in use.

Our days in the northern forests passed all too quickly for they were very happy days. It was a paradise for small mammals and I caught dozens of new and little known species of voles, shrews, wood-mice, rats, picas, squirrels and hares. Moose, roe-deer, wapiti, bear and wild boar were among our larger game. We lived like veritable children of the woods, shooting in the morning and late afternoon, eating and sleeping when we would, careless of the weeks that passed.

On August the fourteenth there came the first

touch of frost. Valleys and forest had been bright with masses of blue-bells, for-get-me-nots, jensens and dozens of other wild flowers but then they quickly began to droop and wither. Blueberries and currants were ripe. By September first it was freezing hard each night. Still we lingered on loath to leave that wild free life. Snow drove us out in mid-September and we crossed the plains again to Kalgan. Coltman's house was the first we had been in for many weeks and that night we could not sleep. The walls oppressed us; we missed the kiss of the night wind on our faces. Unrolling our fur bags we carried them to a grass spot in the courtyard and there slept happily till morning.

Harry Caldwell, the tiger shooting missionary, with whom I had hunted in South China, was waiting in Peking. Almost immediately he and I started northward for the rugged mountains of the Sino-Mongolian frontier for the bighorn sheep and wapiti. Eight magnificent *argali*, including a world's record head, four wapiti, six goral, ten roedeer and two wolves and scores of pheasants, partridges, quail, ducks and geese were our bag for eighteen days of actual shooting.

We were the first foreigners to visit the region for six years because it was infested with bandits and the Chinese authorities would give us no passports. Our base camp for sheep hunting was only five miles from the ancient Mongol city of Kwei-hua-cheng. When the governor found that Harry and I were actually shooting in the mountains he was frantic with fear that we might be killed or captured. He sent an officer to pray us to go away. We categorically refused for there were no bandits.

Then he said he must send soldiers to accompany us into the mountains every day. That was not so good but there was nothing to do. The governor must "save his face." Four of them arrived in full uniform carrying a flag and bugle. We announced that they must be ready to go before daylight. Hardship number one, for Chinese are late sleepers! Our first morning out Harry and I set a terrific pace to the foot hills. After going a thousand feet straight up in the roughest part of the mountains, the soldiers were absolutely exhausted. They simply could not go on. I suggested that they descend to a tiny temple at the base of the peak and await us there. Then we could return together at night and no one would be the wiser. The idea was a life saver. Down they went to spend the day sleeping peacefully in the sunshine while we did our shooting. At night we picked them up and returned to the village with the flag flying and bugle blowing. This farce went on every day during the time we hunted in that vicinity. The governor's "face was saved," the soldiers had a fine rest and we got good shooting. One soon finds out that in China there is a way of getting around almost everything. They are the greatest "compromisers" in the world. If the outward form is observed and no one loses face you can get away with murder.

When we returned to Peking in mid-November I took account of stock. The seven months work had brought a collection of fifteen hundred mammals, all from a region that was virtually new to science. That was important as a tangible result to the Museum authorities and my friends who had helped finance the trip. But the really vital thing was the knowledge I had gained of Mongolia as a theater of work for the great expedition of my dreams.

Professor Osborn had prophesied that the Central Asian plateau would prove to be the place of origin for much of the mammalian life of the northern hemisphere. It was immaterial where we made our first attack.

Mongolia was a part of the indicated region. I knew its physical problems fairly well and had a very clear cut plan for the whole work. Every detail was in my mind for its conception had been gradually developing since my first expedition to the wilderness of northern Korea in 1912.

I was in the prime of life physically and mentally with a good background of Oriental experience and unbounded enthusiasm. The time had come to strike. I was to discover whether or not I had the ability to sell the expedition to the Trustees of the Museum and the public. It would require a lot of money—a quarter of a million dollars at the very least. The Museum, I knew, could give but a small fraction of that amount from its regular funds no matter how keen they were for my plan. Financing it would be up to me. Also, I must personally attend to every detail of organization, equipment, personnel and general publicity. It would be a fairly big job but I was confident because I believed so completely in the value of the work; because I had prepared myself so thoroughly; because every detail was so clear in my mind; but most of all, because I wanted to do it so intensely that I was willing to make any sacrifice. That, to me, is the greatest secret of success. We rented the house in Peking, stored our furniture and sailed for America in January, 1920.

CHAPTER XV

THREE days after my arrival in New York I had luncheon with Professor Osborn in the President's office at the Museum. We talked about general subjects until the coffee. Then the President said: "Well, Roy, what is on your mind? Another expedition, I suppose."

"Yes," I answered. "That's why I came back. It is an expedition that I've been dreaming about for eight years. You are responsible. It is all based on your 1900 prophecy that Central Asia was the incubating region for the land life of Europe and America. I want to test your theory. I want to see if we can find primitive human remains or traces of man's evolution."

"Well," said the President, "how do you propose to undertake it?"·

That was my cue. I began talking as I never had talked before. In two minutes Professor Osborn's eyes were glowing. He stopped smoking and just

245

sat there looking hard at me absorbing every word I said.

"More than that we should try to reconstruct the whole past history of the Central Asian plateau. We ought to learn its geological structure, fossil life, its past climate and vegetation. We should make collections of its living mammals, birds, fish and reptiles. We should map the unexplored and little known regions of the Gobi desert."

"That is a pretty ambitious program," said the Professor. "So far as I am aware no other expedition has ever attempted anything so comprehensive."

"It *is* an ambitious program," I answered, "but I have been thinking about it for eight years. I have every detail planned. If we do it at all it must be on a big scale. I am through with wasting opportunities as small expeditions have to do."

Then I told him about Yunnan. How we had accomplished only one small part of the work there was to do even after we had penetrated to the very heart of a difficult and dangerous region.

"Of course we don't know if there is anything for us in Mongolia," said he. "The Russians have found nothing. What makes you think that we can do better?"

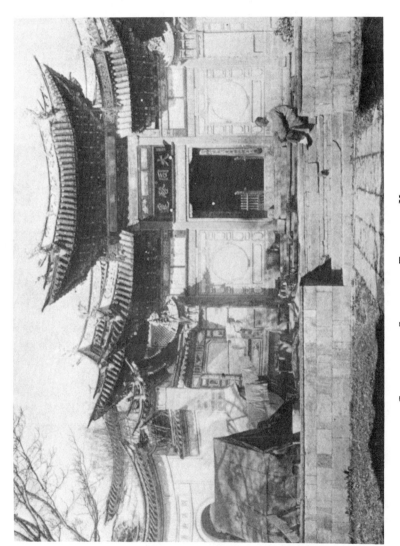

CAMP ON THE STEPS OF A TEMPLE IN YUN-NAN.

TEMPLE AND MONASTERY IN YUN-NAN.

"Just this. The past work has all been too much political and too little scientific. There have been a few good men—Prjevalski, Kozlov, Obrechev— but the others had to produce economic or political results. Science was not the primary aim. No one has attempted to do it the way I plan. Moreover, they have all used camels. They could only average ten or fifteen miles a day. We will have motor cars. We can go a hundred miles a day. We can work at least ten times as fast. We ought to do in one season as much as others have done in ten years."

"How do you know that you can use automobiles in the western Gobi?"

"I don't *know* it. But I believe from all that I have seen and been able to learn about the country that it can be done. It will be largely a matter of preparation. The terrain is mostly fine gravel. I don't think there is much loose sand. We must have every conceivable spare part and motor experts who can repair a car under difficult conditions. Such men exist. We can get them. The rest will be up to us."

"How are you going to transport all your gasoline and supplies? You can't do it in the cars."

"We will have a supporting caravan of camels. It will act exactly like the supply ship to a fleet. The camels must leave far enough in advance to get well out in the desert before we arrive—perhaps six or seven hundred miles. We can carry enough gas and food for that distance. Then they can be sent on ahead or follow behind us as conditions develop."

"What about the scientific staff," asked the Professor, "how do you intend to do the work?"

"We must have a geologist, palæontologist, archæologist, topographer and photographer to start with. I can do the geological work on mammals and birds, but a reptile and fish man will be necessary. We will all work together. It will be a concentration of scientific artillery upon a few definite problems. Every branch of science that can possibly assist us must be represented."

Professor Osborn asked me a great many more questions. At the end of an hour he said:

"Roy, we've got to do it. The plan is scientifically sound. Moreover, it grips the imagination. Finances are the only obstacle. You estimate five years for the expedition and a quarter of a million dollars. That is a good deal of money and there is a severe business depression at present. Of course, the Museum will do all it can, but getting most of the money will be up to you."

I knew that right enough and started in at once. I telephoned Mr. J. P. Morgan for an appointment.

He said to meet him in his library the next morning at nine o'clock. I was there on the second ready to fire the first gun in my campaign for funds.

Talking with Mr. Morgan isn't difficult. He is interested in so many things. He is such an adventurer in spirit and has such a keen, sane mind that in five minutes the romance of the plan had caught his interest. I had brought a map of Central Asia marked with our proposed route. Spread out in front of him he studied it carefully asking dozens of questions; the sort that got at the very fundamentals of the expedition.

Suddenly he straightened up, his eyes bright with excitement: "It's a great plan. What do you want me to do?"

"I need money, Mr. Morgan," I said, "finances are the only thing that stand in the way."

"All right, I'll give you fifty thousand dollars. That ought to help, as a beginning. Now go out and get the rest of it. I'm betting on you."

That was characteristic of the man. Not only had he given me fifty thousand dollars in money but another fifty thousand in confidence. I knew that from that moment he would stand behind me and the expedition because he believed that it was worth doing. In all these years his interest has never waned.

I went back to the Museum walking on air. President Osborn was delighted. We planned a dinner to be given at the University Club where I could tell my story to a group of wealthy men who might be interested. I remember that I sat next to the late Judge E. H. Gary, President of the U. S. Steel Corporation, and that he told me a great deal about his early life. The senior Mr. George F. Baker, President of the First National Bank of New York, was there, even at that time a man nearly eighty years old. My old friend Mr. Sidney M. Colgate, Vice President of Colgate & Co., sat on my left. Mr. John D. Rockefeller, Jr., could not come but his friend and confidential advisor, the late Mr. Starr J. Murphy, was present. Through Mr. Murphy's personal interest Mr. Rockefeller became one of my staunchest supporters.

The late Mr. H. P. Davison and Mr. Thomas W. Lamont of J. P. Morgan & Co., Mr. Childs Frick, Mr. Arthur Curtiss James, Mr. John T. Pratt and perhaps a half a dozen others composed a gathering which read like a page from Who's Who.

I had maps and a few pictures and after dinner told them the plan of the expedition just as I had sketched it to Professor Osborn. All of them were interested. They were the sort of men who were accustomed to handling only big things. This was big enough and unusual enough to grip their imaginations. Nothing was said about money at that dinner. Later, I went to see them in their various offices, and not one failed to do his bit.

Mr. Louis D. Froelick, Editor of *Asia* Magazine, agreed to coöperate with the expedition and he was of great assistance. The American Asiatic Association became a contributor.

Mrs. Willard D. Straight (now Mrs. L. K. Elmhirst) gave a reception at her beautiful house on Fifth Avenue and I told of our plans to about two hundred of New York's most prominent society members. This was followed by a flood of invitations. I remember that I had thirty-two dinners in succession that winter. I moved in a haze of beautiful houses and rich food. It got so that I could hardly remember where I had dined the night before. At each one I told my story, for my job was to interest New York. Every week I spoke at two or three club luncheons, and often lectured in the evening.

In the meantime I wrote a series of magazine articles and a book. It was my third popular volume and was done under difficulties. I used to carry the last sentence and a few blank sheets in my pocket.

While I was having my shoes polished, while riding on street cars, while waiting in offices, any odd moment would produce a few paragraphs. I hardly knew what it was to write an entire chapter consecutively. But somehow it grew and was completed.

When there was sufficient money in sight to be sure that the expedition would materialize it was announced from the American Museum. Mail stories had been sent out with a release date and the day before that, I met the representatives of twenty-one papers and news agencies in the Members' room at the Museum. Next morning the story had the front page of all the great papers throughout the United States. That pleased us enormously for it isn't easy to land on the front page, particularly of a New York daily. It meant that the editors realized it was an expedition of considerable importance and public interest was assured. People believe what the papers tell them. You may say: "I only believe half I read in the newspapers," but subconsciously you believe a good deal more than half. The printed word carries conviction. After all, newspapers are the only way we have of knowing what is going on in the world and, I am happy to say, that in my experience most reporters try to get the real truth. Anyway they did a lot for us.

The thing that caught the popular imagination was our search for primitive human remains. Everyone is interested in where man developed, what he looked like and how he became the dominant creature of the earth.

I was rather appalled at first, for I was afraid it would turn conservative scientists against us. In vain did I try to direct attention to the larger aspects of the work. To our desire to test Osborn's theory of Central Asia as a theatre of mammalian evolution. The public would have none of it. What they wanted was to know about that so-called "Missing Link."

We told everyone that we never could *expect* to find human remains; that the best we could do was to hope. That it was much like looking for the proverbial needle in the haystack. That human bones are so fragile that they are not as readily preserved as are those of larger mammals. That even in the early stages of his evolution man was more intelligent than the animals about him and that he was not as readily trapped in bogs, quicksand and rivers where his remains could be fossilized. That the best scientific opinion pointed to Central Asia as the place of his origin and that all we could do was to concentrate upon the problem in a thoroughly scientific way. That first we should have to reconstruct the past physical conditions of the great plateau before we could feel that we were working in the right place.

All this did not create a ripple in the newspaper world. They just were not interested. Primitive man was what they wanted and anything else bored them exceedingly. Soon we realized that there was nothing for it but to bow to the inevitable and talk Missing Links for all we were worth since it was a definite part of our program.

After the first news announcement the special writers had their turn. By this time I was immersed in details of the expedition and they took hours of time when I had little enough to give. But it was most important because in those stories for Sunday papers the writers had time and space to tell more of our real plans.

Applications to join the expedition came in a deluge. There were a dozen telegrams when I reached my office at ten o'clock the morning of the first announcement and others came every hour. Six or eight men were waiting. One claimed prior consideration for he had read the story at seven in the morning, had hired an aëroplane and flown down from Goshen, New York. That was quite a compliment for in those days one didn't fly all over the place as one does now. He was an artist and unfortunately we didn't need an artist in the beginning of our work.

One of the first telegrams read: "Regarding search for Missing Link, Ouija board offers assistance." The second day a letter arrived from a lady in St. Louis. She said that after reading the news announcement she had communicated with certain spirits, with whom, I judged, she was on familiar terms. They had informed her of a buried city in the Gobi Desert where a record of man's development might be found from the time he crawled on all fours until the dawn of history. It was so amusing that I wrote in return asking if she would be good enough to inquire from her friends, the spirits, about the latitude and longitude of the city as the Gobi was rather a large place. A fortnight later she replied that the spirits were annoyed at my request but had vouchsafed the information that the spot was marked by four large stones half buried in the sand.

As the letters poured in, dozens of men, women and boys made personal application at the Museum. It soon became evident that I must go into close confinement if I was to do any work. My efficient secretary saw most of the applicants and presented me with a list of their qualifications. I could see very few of them myself.

By the end of the first week my mail had assumed alarming proportions. One hundred letters a day was about the average although often there were many more than that. Of course, it was impossible for me to read them. A secretary sorted all the applications from the other business communications. She made a card index with a list of qualifications and in reply sent printed slips saying that the application had been put on file. It may have seemed a cold blooded manner to treat a man who had an intense desire to go, but it was the only possible way to handle the thousands of letters.

As a matter of fact there was very little chance for any applicant because our work was so specialized. I had made up my mind that our scientific staff should consist only of the best men available. All our camp work would be done by natives, so that eliminated all those who had no special scientific training.

The applications naturally fell into three classes. Those from ex-army men, mostly aviators, who could not settle down to the monotony of every day life after the war. Then there were many hundreds from boys fourteen to eighteen years of age to whom life was just opening as a wonderful adventure.

I remember one boy of fourteen whose letter was badly spelled but most amusing. "I want to help you find the Missing Link," he wrote, "I have always been interested in old clothes and things that people wore long ago. I can climb trees and I don't get dizzy. I know you will meet terrible dangers. Probably wild 'can-naballs' will try to eat you. Who knows, I might even save your life. Of course, I probably wouldn't get the chance but I would if I could."

One man wished to act as a waiter and by way of special qualifications said that he owned a tuxedo coat. Another who had been a butcher all his life wanted to go as my personal body-servant.

A thousand or more came from women. Most of the latter were really serious but some were frankly asking for a bit of romance.

One day I heard my secretary exclaim under her breath, while reading the mail, *"Why, the idea."* Then she remarked, "I don't know whether you will consider this amusing or not, but you had better read it and here's the photograph."

The letter was from a woman who said, "I have

already written two books but they haven't been accepted yet. I want to get material for a third—something *occult* and *stirring* and I think I can find it with you. I could go in a secretarial capacity for I have seen your picture in the newspapers and I am sure that you know how to treat a lady.

"But even if you don't need a secretary there are many other things that I can do. Perhaps I could go just as a 'woman friend.' I could create the 'home atmosphere' for you in those drear wastes. I am enclosing my photograph, but could you not have tea with me some day when your work is done? After you have seen me I will leave it with you to judge."

That was the gem of the collection but there were others almost as good. Some in fact spoke right out and called a spade a spade.

At least a dozen came from people who obviously were mentally deranged. They would have been committed to an institution by any jury in the country on that evidence alone. I suppose, altogether the letters gave a pretty good cross-section of humanity. "I learned about humans from them."

The necessary qualities in the men selected for the expedition were about equally divided under the general headings of technical ability and personality.

ANDREWS WITH LEROW SHOT IN YUN-NAN.

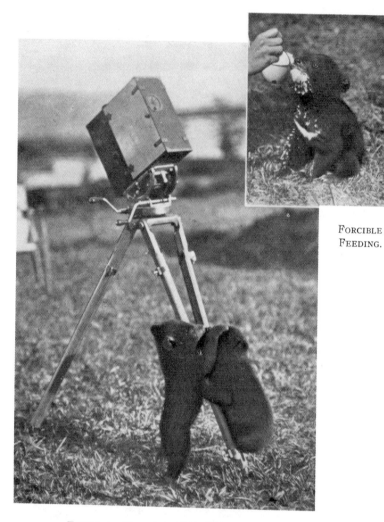

Forcible
Feeding.

Trying to Find Out How It Works.

It was not difficult to learn about the first. A scientist's work speaks for itself and I had determined to have only well known men on the staff. Not only would a high degree of knowledge and experience be required but the association of recognized authorities with the expedition would give its field investigations immediate acceptance by scientific institutions throughout the world.

Personality, by which I mean character, ability to get on with others and to endure disappointments and discomforts, was as important as scientific knowledge.

In the desert we have to create our own little world. There are no newspapers, letters, theatres or other diversions. Whatever we have we must make for ourselves. Day after day we see the same faces, learn every mannerism, the innermost secrets of a man's character. If he is selfish, it is bound to show before very many days have passed. When we are at grips with crude nature, when the struggle to maintain ourselves and do our work against physical odds, is really on, the gloss of civilization quickly drops away. It leaves character bare for all to see. There is very little left to know about a man after you have lived with him in the field for a few weeks under primitive conditions.

I wanted men who would be considerate of their fellows, generous, unselfish, ready to accept the worst with the best. Men so keen on their jobs that hardships would be an incident; men with such steadfastness of purpose that nothing could turn them aside.

I found them and not one has let me down. During four expeditions to the Gobi we have had from six to fifteen men on our foreign staff and not a quarrel. We have lived together in unity and forbearance, in mutual respect and affection. I am just as proud of that record as of the scientific achievements of the expedition.

Nerve strains are hardest to bear. We have had days and weeks of continual sand-storms when our nerves were raw from the never ceasing roar of wind and blasts of yellow sand. When to endure oneself was bad enough but to have others about was torture. Those are the times when character shows, for some silly incident may start a quarrel which will lead to a bitter feud.

I knew a few men who happily combined the qualities of scientific ability and personality and they were invited to go upon the expedition. All of them accepted and our staff for the first year was complete.

My paper plan was to make a base camp for the main party about which each unit could work in a circle. In the meantime an advance party would scout ahead for a new field of operations. As it would not be possible for all of the scientists to find work in the same place at the same time, the expedition would be divided into three or more units, each complete within its own car, equipment, cook and Mongol interpreter. The first year's work was intended to be merely a *reconnaissance* to find out what was in the country. Then the next season would be one of intensive work when we could stay for a considerable time in definite localities.

All this had been planned on paper. It is not always that advance plans materialize in the field without considerable change, but in this case they did. I had become so thoroughly familiar with the general conditions of the country we were to explore that I knew what physical conditions to expect.

The matter of equipment was important. As I am not a believer in unnecessary hardships I proposed to make ourselves as comfortable as possible while we were in the base camp. Folding tables and chairs, camp beds and other gear did much to keep us happy and physically fit. We had plenty of hardships at times but never when they could be avoided. Food was something of a problem. We could get all of the game we needed in the desert but nothing else. Egg powder, dried milk and dried fruits and vegetables were most important. With Dr. Kellogg, of the Battle Creek Sanitarium, I discussed the relative food value of certain products and received the latest scientific advice.

As a result we have had hardly a case of illness during any of our expeditions. A surgeon was necessary as an insurance policy more than anything else. Gun-shot wounds and broken bones are always likely to occur. But we have been very lucky. In the first three expeditions nothing happened. In the fourth, I would have died from a bullet in the leg, and one of our motor experts would have lost his life from a knife wound, had we not been prepared with a competent surgeon.

We took a radio set with us but only to receive time signals for checking our chronometers. This was necessary to obtain exact longitude observations. I am not a believer in radio for an expedition such as ours. Most of the men brought their wives and families with them to wait in Peking until their return from Mongolia. Suppose we were a thousand miles out in the desert and some one received word that his wife or one of his children was dead or dying! He could do nothing. It would be impossible to return and his summer's work would be ruined. Better be ignorant of home affairs until his return since he could be of no assistance in any event. I know that all my men are more contented to drop entirely out of the world than to keep in touch with it at a distance. Doubtless it is necessary for some expeditions, but for us certainly not. We have tried both ways. It is remarkable what a relief it is to vanish from the world of everyday and how philosophical one becomes. Moreover it is interesting to find how little of real importance happens in an ordinary month.

Sometimes big events occur and one does not learn of them until a long time after reaching civilization. I remember that I did not know of President Harding's death until three weeks after the expedition had returned to Peking. I first discovered it in a news dispatch about *President Coolidge!* Harding had died some months before we returned and the sensation was already a thing of the remote past. When you ask for news usually you will be told only those events which have occurred during the last two or three weeks.

By the time we were ready to sail for China in

March, 1921, the money for the expedition had all been raised, the staff selected, the equipment shipped and my book published. Also I was almost a nervous wreck. It took several months of Oriental quiet and polo in Peking to put me right again but after all it was worth the price. The expedition of my dreams was an accomplished fact. Would the field work be a success?

It was a tremendous gamble for the basis was only a scientific theory. No matter how well we were organized, or what good men we had if the specimens were not there we could not find them. Everyone told us that our motor transport would be a hopeless failure. Scientists said that we might as well look for fossils in the Pacific Ocean as to expect to find them in the sand swept wastes of the Gobi Desert. I was backing my own opinion against that of many older men. But they did not know the interior of Mongolia and I did. Still no one realized more fully than I what a chance we took. If the expedition were a failure I never could face those loyal men and women whom I had persuaded to back it with their faith and dollars. In that event I knew it would be my "swan song" in exploration. I remarked as much to Professor Osborn at our last meeting.

He put his hand on my shoulder and said "Nonsense, Roy. The fossils are there, I know they are. Go and find them."

So we sailed away from San Francisco on the new ship "Golden State" for my land of Heart's Desire.

CHAPTER XVI

RENTING a house does not sound like a very complicated business but just try to do it in Peking! Unless you have a sense of humor and a certain determination you will give it up and live in the hotel. We arrived on April 4, 1921, in the midst of a terrific dust storm and house renting became my first job. It was somewhat simplified because I knew exactly the place for the expedition's headquarters. It was a beautiful old palace belonging to a Manchu prince. I had seen it first when it was occupied by my friend, Dr. G. E. Morrison. He had died a year previously and the place was vacant.

Almost all really serious business in China is done through an intermediary. He brings both parties together, if he can, in the matter of price and collects a substantial squeeze as an honorarium. It is not until the final negotiations that the principals see each other.

When my prospective landlord realized that he

had extracted the very last dollar that I would pay in the way of rent, we came to terms. The negotiations that far had taken three weeks. Twice they had been broken off and the middle-man was frantic because he saw his commission vanishing. Another two weeks were consumed in making out the lease, since it had to be most carefully scrutinized for a possible double meaning to the Chinese characters in which it was written. It is not unusual for the landlord to slip in a character or two which will nullify all the concessions that have been made.

We got the lease signed after five weeks but then I found that we could not occupy the house for another four weeks unless I was prepared to pay a month's rent to the police in "squeeze." They would not even let me put a box inside. I could either delay the expedition for a month or pay the squeeze. I paid.

In order to get the water turned on I had to give forty-five dollars squeeze to the water company and pay for the meter in addition. The electric light company demanded one hundred and fifty dollars squeeze for the privilege of buying their light. I finally got off with only a hundred.

Thus it went through every phase of getting the house ready to occupy. Squeeze, squeeze, squeeze!

You rebel and say that you won't pay. All right, you live in a hotel. You might as well realize at the beginning that you will pay a squeeze on every item that comes into your house from five coppers worth of carrots to the rugs on your floor. Somebody gets his commission whether you like it or not. You can't live in China without paying squeeze. It is a national custom. The amount you pay depends largely upon yourself.

When I rented my house I discovered that a Chinese landlord is responsible only for the walls and the roof. He is supposed to keep those in re-pair but all else you do yourself.

Every house is surrounded by a wall which en-closes a series of courtyards. The whole is called a compound. My compound occupies an acre and has eight courts, with buildings on three sides of each. Of course there is no upstairs; everything is on one level. Every room is floored with stone, cold and damp—wooden floors you must put in your-self and they are expensive. Bathrooms are non-existent. You make your own bathrooms or you go without. I put in three which cost five hundred dollars gold, each. They are nice bathrooms, too, but as there is no sewerage system in Peking each one must have its own septic tank. When you give

ANDREWS ENCOURAGES A SMALL SHAN BOY TO FACE THE CAMERA.

THE BURMESE YELLOW GIBBON.

up the house, of course, you get nothing in return from the landlord for all your improvements. That is part of his squeeze. I had to make a garage for five cars, stables for six ponies, a motion picture laboratory and dozens of other adaptations to fit it for the work of the expedition.

Our house had one hundred and sixty-one rooms, or *gin,* when Dr. Morrison took it over from the prince. That means that the different buildings were divided by partitions into one hundred and sixty-one cubicles. In these lived the dozens of servants and retainers as well as the prince's concubines. He had thirty "concs." That was what he rated and no self-respecting prince could do with less. When he went to court they all trailed along to make up an imposing procession. The concs that got on well together lived on intimate terms. Those who were inclined to quarrel with others were put by themselves. Hence all the courtyards. In a great house of that kind people could live for months without seeing each other since the bound feet of a Chinese woman restricted her activities to a very circumscribed space. Of course Morrison tore out most of the partitions throwing a dozen or more cubicles into a single great room. There are about forty rooms in the house as I occupy it today.

When we left China in 1920 we had found positions for all our old servants. Before we returned in 1921 I rented, by cable, a furnished house for three months from a friend, Lt.-Col. Smallwood. Also, I agreed to take over all his servants during that time.

As we stepped off the train in Peking the first to greet us were eight or ten of our old servants. As soon as they heard that we were returning all had immediately abandoned their jobs. In their simple minds there was no question but that we would want them back. They had become just as definitely a part of our household as our own children. I did want them but they would not fit in with the new *ménage*. So for three months I had to give them a vacation on full pay.

In China you have many servants for each one does only a single kind of work. There are from eighteen to twenty around my house. The Number One Boy is the butler and if you are wise you will let him hire all the other servants. Then he is responsible, and if anything is lost or stolen he can be held legally accountable. Moreover, he receives their first month's salary from all those he hires as a commission for getting them the place. Wages vary somewhat with the size of the house and the part of China but in Peking the usual salary for a Number One is ten dollars gold a month. The other boys receive six or seven dollars a month. Coolies about five. All servants feed themselves in theory. Actually they eat a good deal of your food such as rice, vegetables, tea, etc.

Our house is large and I never know exactly how many people I have, for at least a third of them are "learn pidgin" servants; they are learning to do some particular work. The height of a Chinese's desire is to get a job and then hire someone else to do it for him at a less wage. For instance I noticed that the gate-man whose life work consists in opening and shutting the big front gates never was there at night. Always a young fellow turned out when I returned late. One night I asked him who he was! "I belong learn-pidgin gate-man," said he. Learning to open and shut gates! He received two dollars a month and a place to sleep from the actual holder of the position. Some day he might aspire to be a full-fledged, experienced gate-man.

We have three cooks but I pay only one. The other two are learn-pidgin boys who work for the training they receive. The head cook really acts as a supervisor in the kitchen. All the servants get a good deal more than their salary from the various kinds of squeeze. It is divided up on a regular system. The Number One Boy is the principal benefactor. No purchase comes into the house without ten percent going to him. Often we have friends staying with us who spend a good deal of money in buying curios and then the Number One reaps a harvest. On coal he extracts two dollars a ton squeeze; the stove coolie gets his from the fire-wood. The cook does fairly well for himself on the groceries, vegetables and meat. The *mafus* (grooms) on feed for the ponies; the chauffeur by stealing my gasoline; the outside coolies on brooms, etc., which are never used.

All this is a perfectly recognized custom. It is not considered dishonest by the Chinese. Several times I have had servants apply for a position and when asked why they left their last place they frankly told me that they could not get enough squeeze to live. Newcomers to China hate to think they are being "done" by their servants. It gets on their nerves and they try to eliminate squeeze. You might just as well try to stop an oncoming wave with your hands. You exhaust yourself and get nowhere. All you can do is to keep the squeeze down to reasonable limits. I allow ten percent. When the bills begin to run up, I make a terrific row and expenses abruptly drop.

But it is a delightful Aladdin's Lamp sort of existence. You say what you want and things happen. It is best not to inquire *how* they are to be done. Leave all that to your Number One and if he is up to his job there will be no trouble.

We often give dinner parties of twenty-five or thirty people although our silver and glass are sufficient for only half that number. I never ask where the rest is coming from but it always appears. I simply tell my Boy who is dining here that night and he borrows whatever is necessary from the servants of some of the guests. We have some particularly beautiful candlesticks and fish plates and I'm sure to meet them wherever we dine in Peking if it is a big party.

One never worries about bringing home extra guests without notice for any meal in Peking. There always seems to be enough food. Time after time I have returned for tiffin with three or four people when the servants expected our usual luncheon of only two. There is never even a look of consternation on the Boy's face. Perhaps a little longer will be occupied with cocktails before tiffin is announced but there is always a good meal.

One evening two of us decided to dine at the Club where dinner is served only after an hour's notice. We called Ginger, the Number One Boy.

"Can catch dinner tonight, Ginger?"

"You wait a few minutes, I see." Fifteen minutes later dinner was announced. We had six or seven courses including roast Peking duck. We were really curious that time.

"Ginger, where you catch this dinner?"

"Oh, master, that very easy. Mr. Faxon telephone he not come home tonight. I catch 'im duck his house."

Faxon lived next to the Club and it so happened that his boy was in the kitchen when we asked for the unexpected dinner. He got a little squeeze for delivering it and Faxon never knew the difference.

Living is made so very easy in China that one becomes hopelessly spoiled. There never is a servant problem. If a Number One Boy is unsatisfactory usually all the servants must go with him for they are all his henchmen. You can't engage others until the old ones are actually out of the house. After they have gone a new lot will be installed within a few hours.

I never have lived in any country where one can have better food than in Peking. All winter long an amazing variety of game is in the markets. Snipe, wood cock, ducks of half a dozen species, geese, pheasants, quail, partridges, gazelle, roedeer and wild boar. All of it very cheap. I think we pay ten cents each for snipe; for pheasant fifty cents. Eggs average about seventy-five cents a hundred; chickens, thirty cents.

Fish is not so good in North China, although there is plenty of it brought to us from the sea at Tientsin. Prawns, huge shrimps, six or eight inches long, arrive in April. They are more delicious than lobster.

Of course we are handicapped when it comes to vegetables. Unless they are grown in your own garden you ought never to eat uncooked vegetables. Be careless, and dysentery or other intestinal diseases are the inevitable result. Beets, carrots, spinach, cauliflower, cabbage, or anything that can be cooked, are perfectly safe. We get delicious strawberries in season but always scald or wash them with potassium permanganate before eating.

Most of all, drinking water should be well boiled. When I return to America it is difficult to become accustomed to drinking out of a tap. In China bottles of boiled water are always kept on ice.

One might think that such precautions would be

inconvenient but they really are not. After a few weeks, they become a habit.

We get the best French wines, and whiskey, beer, ginger-ale, anything that comes in a bottle, at very moderate cost. In the old days drink was the curse of the East. Today it is much less so.

Before the Nationalists moved the Capital to Nanking in 1928, Peking was the most interesting residence city of the world with the exception, perhaps, of Constantinople. There are about two thousand foreigners here including the Legations and nationals of almost every country. We are a very cosmopolitan community but rather a small one for all that.

Of course, the social life centers about the Legations and the Club. Peking is above all a social place. Something is going on every moment and that something is usually interesting. Dancing at the hotel, or, in the summer, on the roof garden is the usual procedure after dinner. We have shadow pictures or a Chinese conjurer. The old *Ega-lang-dang* man is as much a part of Peking as is the Chien Men gate. He has been here since the oldest inhabitant can remember.

One part of Peking's community plays a good deal of bridge, poker or mahjong. I do not see much of them for my friends are the outdoor people—those who ride, play polo or tennis, hunt to hounds, and race.

During the spring and autumn race meets, the foreign banks close and all Peking is *en fête*. Most of us have our own race ponies, train them ourselves and the jockeys are gentlemen riders. It is a family affair but the betting is heavy and a good deal of money changes hands. In Shanghai the sweepstakes on the Champion's race amounts to several hundred thousand dollars.

Polo goes on from the first of April to mid-November. We are all very keen and take our sport most seriously. In fact, much more seriously than business, as a rule. No one works too hard. Work is a sort of necessary evil which makes the play possible. If you go for a business call to a man's office at least half the time is consumed with a discussion of polo, racing or the latest political sensation. That is the custom of the country. One never immediately begins a business conversation with a Chinese. It would be considered distinctly impolite. One must talk about general subjects for awhile and drink a little tea before broaching the real object of one's call. Foreigners have fallen into the same habit.

Many of us rent a temple in the hills or near the race course for a country place. My temple is a lovely spot, filled with great cedar trees, beautiful flowers and singing birds. It is very, very old; about five hundred years, I think. I rent it from the village. Just how the elders distribute the money I do not know but every year, three dignified old men make a pilgrimage to my Peking house. We drink tea together, discuss matters of public interest and then I give them two hundred and forty dollars, the year's rent.

It works very well from every standpoint. If any one wants to worship at the temple we make no objections for they only come to burn a joss stick or two. It is always interesting because ours is a very special temple. It rejoices in the name of the "Temple of the Hopeful Fecundity" and is where women come to pray for a child. Of course, they always want a boy; girls are a distinct liability in a Chinese household. They eat as much as a boy, do little work and when they get married worship the tablets of their husband's family.

In the main room of our temple a great gilded idol sits calmly on a lotus flower while two smaller ones keep guard on either side. A huge bronze gong rests on the altar. The suppliant purchases a few sticks

NATIVE HUNTER SPYING FOR SHEEP IN SHENSI MOUNTAINS.

Mongol Hunter with a Trophy, Big Horn Shensi Sheep.

of incense, strikes the gong three times to call attention to her prayer, bows low and murmurs her request. She gives an offering of food or coppers to the temple priest (who also acts as my caretaker) and goes away happy in the thought that a boy is sure to come.

The fact that foreigners occupy the temple does not worry Chinese in the slightest. They have no reverence for their temples as we do for our churches. Neither do they particularly revere the idols. They think they can fool their gods. One sees it in a dozen ways. For instance, they often give a bad name such as, "Cow Dung," to a favorite child. This is to fool the devil that kills children and make him think that the family care little for the boy.

I wanted to buy a small image on a temple altar one day but the priests would not sell it until they had plastered mud over the eyes of the god. They explained that then he could not see them take it away.

Almost all the temples near the race course and in the Western Hills are rented to foreigners, whole or in part. Some of them are of vast extent and only two or three courtyards are taken over.

I used my temple as a week-end place. Since it

is in the midst of the hunting country we go there every Sunday before the point-to-point hunt. At race meets fifteen or twenty people come for tiffin. During the spring or summer I often retire there when I want to write quietly for a few days.

I know of no place in the world where there is an atmosphere of such utter peace as in a Chinese temple. The twisted old cedar trees, the flowers and the priests themselves belong to another world. Nothing seems of much importance except to drowse in the sun and watch the flowers and birds.

Some years ago, four of us took a large temple together. It was called the "Temple of the High Spirited Insects"—no one could explain just why the name. As we were all riding people we soon became known as the "Insects." We had an Insect polo team with spiders embroidered on our shirts; an Insect racing stable; at hunts an Insect was always on the card and we swept the board at gymkhanas.

There are many lovely spots near Peking. Often in the golden days of autumn we will have a riding picnic. After a ten mile gallop over the brown fields, we arrive at a temple or some selected spot where the Boys are waiting with tiffin. They have gone by motor or donkeys, carrying everything for an eight course luncheon from cocktails to coffee. Such is Peking life.

As in most small communities gossip flows like wine. Everybody knows what everyone else is doing and broadcasts it to the world. The scandals that take place are amazing. They couldn't happen anywhere else on earth except in Peking with its cosmopolitan foreign group which is thrown together in the easy comradeship of the East. You can't mix together men and women of a dozen different nationalities in a city of leisure and pleasure without expecting complications. Sometimes the "affairs" have had most unfortunate results but as a rule they are considered pretty lightly.

Peking seldom takes anything seriously. That is its great salvation. It laughs over tragedies, treats Chinese politics with the amusement they deserve and makes war a social function.

In the spring of 1926 we were confined within the city walls. The gates were barred and sandbagged, the Chinese panicky, the foreign population having a glorious time. Every morning promptly at ten o'clock an aëroplane sailed out of the south, dropped a few bombs on the city and flew back again to Chang Tso-lin's lines. The roof of the Peking Hotel was the best place from which to see the show.

289

"Bombing breakfast" became the newest social diversion. A dozen guests would be invited to breakfast in the hotel at nine o'clock. At five minutes to ten they would adjourn to the roof, watch the plane do its stuff and then jump into motor cars to inspect the scene of devastation. As they were small bombs filled with black powder the damage was slight. Usually a coolie or two would be the only casualties. They never killed any soldiers.

The Chien Men railway station near the American Legation was a favorite objective of the airman and the Legation staff began to get a little nervous. It was quite obvious that the bomber was trying to avoid the Legation Quarter but his aim was so poor that an "egg" might land in the compound at any time.

One morning I got a bit too close to it for comfort. I had given a bombing breakfast myself and was particularly disgusted because the plane did not appear. At eleven o'clock I went to the Hsichihmen station to make arrangements for sending our equipment to Mongolia. Just as I drove into the broad plaza in front of the station a plane roared overhead. There was a scattering of pedestrians when a bomb landed with a terrific crash thirty yards to the right of us. Fortunately we were saved from the flying fragments by a high mud wall. I stepped on the gas intending to get into the station for protection but a second bomb landed just in front of the car. Since we were both going in the same direction, I decided to let him win the race.

Jumping out of the car I made for an armoured train standing on the tracks. My Chinese Boy, Lo, backed up against a wall. With a dozen Chinese I crawled under the train and stretched out between the steel wheels parallel with the axles. Suddenly a bomb exploded with a deafening report not fifteen feet from my shelter. The iron fragments "pinged" against the car wheels like rain and I never knew how small I could make myself until that moment. A few seconds later two others crashed almost simultaneously on the opposite side of the train. One iron slug came in at an angle and buried itself within two inches of my face. I dug it out and burned my fingers nicely for it was red hot.

After a few minutes I crawled out thinking that the raid was ended. But the plane had only circled and was directly above us. Before I could duck back under the train a bomb exploded a few feet away right in front of a Chinese woman. It blew her head off as neatly as though it had been severed with a knife. Another bomb landed in front of the wall where my Boy had been standing and killed four men. He only escaped because he had at last decided to obey my calls and come under the car.

The airman was evidently trying to get that particular train for he dropped fourteen bombs within a few feet of it. Luckily he did not land a direct hit.

We were having rather a lively time, what with the noise and smoke and groans of the people who had been injured. I was worried about a huge tank belonging to the Standard Oil Co. which contained twenty-four thousand gallons of petroleum. It was only a short distance away and had a bomb struck the tank we would have had a most beautiful conflagration.

After the 'plane left I went up to the station and tried to transact my business. It couldn't be done, for while we were there the airman returned and gave us another deluge. Evidently the vicinity of the railroad was a pretty unhealthy place and I made a dash for safety in my motor. It so happened that I was the only foreigner who was in real danger during any of the raids.

CHAPTER XVII

UNTIL three years ago Chinese wars were an *opera bouffe*. Now they are more serious. In those days a foreigner was perfectly safe no matter if he happened to get between the fighting lines. A foreign flag was sacred. Now it is an excuse to fire.

In the autumn of 1924 a war was in progress between Chang Tso-lin and Wu Pei-fu. It had centered about a hundred miles northeast of Peking. I wanted to go to the Eastern Tombs, eighty-two miles from the Capital to test some of the new motors for my forth-coming expedition to Mongolia. We took three cars and nine people including Brigadier-General Frank McCoy and the daughter and niece of the American Minister.

We were to travel over a road which led up to the northern front and I knew there would be some troops moving on it. I must confess however, that I didn't expect to find an army with all its guns, ammunition, food and equipment. The road was narrow and it was impossible to avoid frightening the mules at times even though we did our best to be careful. But when a gun or a cart went off into the ditch the soldiers seldom cursed us, although they did fairly well at the mules.

At one village which we could not circle, the only passage was solidly blocked by men, carts and animals halted for tiffin. I approached the officer in charge and told him that we were on the way to the Eastern Tombs. Would it be too much to ask to make way for us?

"Certainly," said he, "I'll send the carts on at once," and so he did.

During the whole trip we never were asked who we were, where we were going, whether we had any credentials or even passports. At noon, and again just before dark we passed through two encampments, threading our way between the tents without a challenge even though we were less than fifty miles from the front lines. I do not think that General McCoy would have believed it had he not been with us. That any army actually on the way to the front would let a picnic party pass over a road blocked by troops and heavy transport was almost unbelievable. Of course it was the little American flag on each car and the fact that we were foreigners that kept us from being questioned. Still it was a pretty casual way to take a war, even if we didn't look suspicious.

In 1924 there were about a thousand soldiers, the remnants of a defeated army, scattered over the Mongolian plateau just north of Kalgan. Since they could only exist by robbery their presence became a menace to the general in command of the area. He promised that all those who came into Kalgan and surrendered their weapons would be forgiven and sent to their respective homes.

Between five and six hundred took him at his word. As each man was disarmed in Kalgan he was locked in a steel box car. Happy at the thought of going home they sang when the train pulled out. But it only went a half a mile and then backed into the station again. One by one the cars were opened and the occupants confronted by the general's soldiers with leveled rifles. Forty at a time were taken out, marched to the stone bridge in the center of the town and lined up on the parapet. Soldiers with automatic pistols and rifles shot them in their heads. The bodies toppled off into the half dry river bed. All day the slaughter went on for the murderers had to refresh themselves between batches with tea and cigarettes.

About five hundred and fifty men were butchered before night. No one knows the exact figure. The river bed was a frightful sight for many of the victims were not killed outright. They crawled about with broken legs and arms and other soldiers amused themselves by taking pot shots at the wounded. Only one man escaped. He had been stunned by a bullet which ploughed along the side of his head and when he recovered consciousness in the river bed had sense enough to lie motionless. His leg was broken but that night he crawled into a friend's compound and remained hidden.

I did not happen to be in Kalgan on the day of the massacre but arrived a week later. Several of my friends had witnessed the entire proceeding from the British American Tobacco Co.'s house. The horror of it was still fresh in their minds.

This was the second incident of the kind that has occurred in Kalgan. In the other the general carried the farce even further. He promised that not only would the men be sent home if they surrendered but that they would each be given five dollars. The money was duly paid and the victims herded into open flat cars. The train was stopped in a railway cut not far from Kalgan where machine guns had been posted. They swept the cars clear of every living being. Then guards searched the bodies to recover the five dollars which had been given each trusting soul.

Politicians must use discrimination as to where they accept invitations to dine. The favourite method of eliminating a political rival is to invite him to dinner and shoot him by way of dessert. But if you would avoid public criticism you must be particularly careful to kill him *after* dinner. It is extremely bad form to shoot any guest before he has been well fed. Not long ago a prominent general disposed of an enemy in this way but did it during the tea drinking preceding the feast. He was most bitterly censured even by those who believed that the victim had received his just desserts.

We who live in China have become so accustomed to such events that it does no more than furnish a few hours' interesting speculation as to what it will mean in the political situation. When it is reported in Europe and America it does not create a ripple. Chinese names are so difficult to remember and their politics are so complicated anyway that the public can't be bothered with the premature demise of a single individual or the treachery of a few generals.

Every change in the local political aspect in any

part of China produces a series of executions. The new gentleman in control proceeds to rid himself of all those who might make trouble by the effective method of a firing squad or the headsman's knife. For a week or two the grisly business goes on. Often the heads are hung on telephone poles in various parts of the city or exhibited in small bamboo cages as a warning to others.

Usually the executions are performed at certain definite places but sometimes they happen right in the middle of the street. I cannot forget one day when looting started in Peking only a short distance from my house. The authorities in charge of the city had given very definite instructions to the gendarmes charged with maintaining order. I was driving up a broad street called Lung Fu Ssu when a terrific commotion started in three small shops. A dense crowd blocked the way. Suddenly there was a rush and four men were dragged into the street by a dozen gendarmes. They were made to kneel almost in front of my car while one of the police lopped off their heads in less than three minutes. It was done so quickly that I hardly knew what was happening and it certainly did stop the looting. The bodies were left in the middle of the street for three days.

TIMBERED HILLS IN MONGOLIA.

TWO MEANS OF TRANSIT IN MONGOLIA.

Personally, I loathe seeing a man beheaded. The public execution ground in Peking is just opposite the Temple of Heaven where I often ride. One summer I stopped going there for every time I drove down the street some poor wretch was on the way to his death. Either he was being paraded, half naked and bound, in an open cart or marched along in the midst of a squad of soldiers. It was so sickening that I decided to ride north of the city walls where one could be fairly certain of not meeting such processions.

Of course, everyone discusses politics in China and almost everyone is perfectly certain that he knows the only real remedy for the chaos which has existed in the country for so many years. He figures out exactly what is going to happen and when. He is right about once in twenty times. The trouble is that the Chinese do not think as we Westerners do. A foreigner can work out a succession of events according to Occidental logic. Such and such must happen and such and such will be the inevitable corollary. He is amazed and rather hurt to discover that what he has so confidently predicted doesn't occur at all. Instead a new bomb is suddenly exploded in the political arena and the entire situation is completely changed overnight. Nevertheless it is a very amusing puzzle to study and furnishes exciting discussions about our tables and at the club. There are three main topics which are certain to occupy the largest part of the conversation at any ordinary Peking dinner party, to wit: ponies, Chinese politics and prohibition in America. All that a hostess needs to do is to interject a few remarks apropos of any of these subjects to keep the conversational ball merrily rolling until it is time to leave for dancing at the hotel.

General Feng Yu-hsiang made a considerable stir a few years ago by professing Christianity. He became known as the "Christian General" and strenuously advocated his beliefs. He baptized his soldiers by regiments and taught them hymns. Everyday I used to hear marching feet outside my compound and then a sudden burst of "Onward Christian Soldiers" or "Praise God from Whom all Blessings Flow." The religious part of it was of real help to one of our prominent Peking residents on the day of Feng's *coup d' état*, at Peking in 1924. He and his wife were coming in from the race course when they found themselves stopped by soldiers and refused entrance at one of the gates. My friend emitted a veritable tidal wave of English which was unintelligible and produced no effect. He gathered breath for another volley and at the end his wife solemnly remarked, "Hallelujah." Instantly the soldiers drew aside and waved them on. They probably thought that he had been delivering a sermon and that this was the benediction!

There was much bustle in the Legations when Peking was occupied by Feng. One never knows what may happen and it is always wise to be on the safe side. Provision is made to house all foreigners inside the walls of the Legation Quarter if there is serious looting or disturbance from unpaid soldiers. Each Legation keeps a list of its nationals but these were not always up to date. One man was informed by letter that in case of trouble he was to call for a lady who had been reposing in the cemetery for eighteen months!

The third day after Feng Yu-hsiang's *coup d' état* in 1924 the telephone and telegraph services in Peking were renewed and steps taken to start a train service to Tientsin. According to the 1900 Protocol the Chinese must allow the foreign nations to keep open the railroad communications to Tientsin and the sea. Therefore an International train, its engine decked with various flags, started to the capital under the command of an American officer. Only those passengers could travel on it who had a permit from the Legations and it was strongly guarded by foreign soldiers.

Wu Pei-fu did what we had expected and moved some of his troops toward Peking.

They intrenched themselves at a place called Yang-tsun, not far from Tientsin and desultory fighting took place for a week. The train was fired upon as it passed the lines and one bullet smashed through the dining car missing the cook's head by a few inches and nearly hitting the cashier. The passengers were unanimous in agreeing that the cook should have been killed for serving such atrocious food and the cashier likewise because he insisted on full price for it.

That night the train happened to be in charge of a French officer who spoke no English or Chinese. His interpreter was a huge coal black Senegalese. Near the front lines soldiers stopped the train and one of them scrutinized the name cards of several passengers by the light of a lantern. Suddenly the Senegalese appeared, roaring out in Chinese, "What's the trouble? Why do you stop the train?" The soldier looked up to see the black face six inches from his own. Never before had he seen a negro. With a yell of fright he leaped back and shouted, "Go, go, go quickly."

In 1920 when Wu Pei-fu drove out the Anfu party, Peking was isolated for some time before an International train was sent out. Of course there may have been diplomatic reasons for getting through to Tientsin, but the only one which we heard, and certainly the most plausible, was that the whiskey and soda in the Capital had given out. How could the beleagured foreigners be expected to sit on the roof garden of the hotel and watch the war in the heat of a mid-summer night without whiskey and soda? It just couldn't be tolerated! The fact remains that the train went and that it brought back the necessary "makings."

It was in 1922 that a part of Wu Pei-fu's army camped on the race course just at the time of the Spring Meeting. There was great indignation among the foreign community, for Peking takes its sport very seriously. At the Club feeling rose higher and higher still with every cocktail. If the Chinese wanted to have war and it amused them to do so, all right. But it was quite another thing when they let their dashed war interfere with our race meet. It was a bit too thick and we wouldn't stand for it!

So the Stewards were delegated to call upon Wu Pei-fu and hint delicately, but withal plainly, that it would be an extremely popular act if he transferred his war elsewhere. Wu said he figured that it might be done and within a few days the army was removed. But he didn't go very far and those who went out for the early morning training were met by a soldier carrying a sign on which was printed in English "Please make detour. This way have got one war."

On October 15, 1924, the railroad was blocked by troop trains going up to the Shan-hai-kuan front. I had a pony that had come straight from Mongolia to Tientsin and I could not get him to Peking; so did one of my friends, the Commander of the American Legation Guard. The races were the next day and we were in the state of nerves that every horse owner can understand. A telegram from Tientsin said that the ponies had been put on a train but no one knew whether it would start at all and if it did how many hours it would require for it to reach Peking. Therefore, I telephoned the Ministry of Communications and explained matters. They said they quite understood and that orders would be issued to give a clear line for the train bringing the ponies. It was done and they arrived at four o'clock on the morning of the races. One of them won the "Maidens"—but it wasn't mine!

CHAPTER XVIII

IT is unfortunate for Peking that the political center has been transferred to Nanking. It is vain to predict whether or not it will remain there but in the meantime it has taken much interest away from our dear old city. With it has gone business and many of the oldest firms have closed their doors. Peking has become only a shell of its former self socially and China is fast losing its attractions as a place of foreign residence. The change began in 1926. Then all tradition and good form was knocked into a cocked hat by the conduct of war. Not only did the Chinese fight in the north during the winter but they killed quite a lot of people. These things just were not done in the past and we began to realize that the old order changeth. Moreover, a foreign flag suddenly lost its significance as a protection. Rather, it became like a red rag to the proverbial bull.

I had a little personal experience which gave me

and all the men of my expedition a real jolt. Feng Yu-hsiang, the so-called Christian General, was having rather a lively war with Chang Tso-lin. It had started the previous October down near Shanghai and spread like a flame to the north. The severest fighting took place during December and January near Tientsin. By April first when I arrived, Chang occupied Tientsin but Feng had fallen back upon Peking.

For weeks there had been no railway traffic between the two cities. The Powers protested. The Chinese told them to go jump in the lake, or words to that effect. That was all wrong for the 1900 Protocol provides that communication from Peking to the sea shall be kept open. Still the fact remained that the only way to reach the capital was by the motor road. McKenzie Young drove down to meet me. Returning we discovered that the road had been mined in thirteen places. It was necessary to drive right across the mines and we both found it rather a jumpy business. Leaving Tientsin we passed out of Chang's lines through a wide "no man's land" and into the rearguard of Feng's army. No active fighting was going on at the time but it was a decidedly unsafe road to travel. Soldier stragglers roamed all along the way robbing whenever they had the opportunity. But we were lucky and reached Peking without serious difficulty.

Two days later I was dining with the American Minister when firing began just outside the city and we all adjourned to the roof of the Peking Hotel. Machine guns showed in a steady stream of light along the southern horizon punctuated by the wide flashes of heavy guns.

The American Military Attaché told us that Feng had begun a new offensive and might even push Chang's army back to Tientsin. But the usual thing happened. One of Feng's generals was bought off by the opposing side and the advance became a retreat.

I had to get through to Tientsin and made a try for it the next day with three members of the expedition, Shackelford, Hill and Beckwith. We thought that a large American flag on the car would protect us as it had done in former years.

The gates of Peking were heavily guarded but the soldiers let us pass. Carts were already coming into the city loaded with grain, camp gear and soldiers. Cavalry streamed by and then thousands upon thousands of infantry. They were retiring in good order and seemed most cheerful. An officer told me that Chang Tso-lin's troops had taken

Tungchow, fourteen miles from Peking and were looting the city but that no fighting was taking place.

We drove on slowly and eventually passed beyond the rear of the retreating army. For three or four miles the countryside was deserted, houses closed and all as quiet as the grave. We were five or six hundred yards from the ancient marble bridge at Tungchow when there came the sharp crack of a rifle and a bullet struck beside the front wheel. A second later a mass of soldiers appeared on the road and bullets began spattering around us like hailstones. They had opened fire with a machine gun but it was aimed too low and the bullets were kicking the dust just in front of us. The soldiers could see the American flag plainly enough but that made not the slightest difference.

Fortunately at this particular spot the road was wide enough for the car to be turned and I swung it about in record time. The bullets now were buzzing like a swarm of bees just above our heads. Forty yards down the road a sharp curve took us out of sight of the machine gun. The other men crouched in the bottom of the car. Since I was driving I could see all the fun. It was a pretty rough road but the speedometer showed fifty miles an hour as

BUDDHIST PILGRIMS EN ROUTE TO A TEMPLE.

MONGOLIAN BRONCHO BUSTERS.

THE MONGOLS ARE NOT NOTED FOR THEIR CLEANLINESS!

we went back. The ride became an exciting one. All the houses which had seemed so peaceful actually were occupied by the advance guards of Fengtien soldiers. They had let us pass because of the American flag but when they heard the firing in our rear and saw us returning at such a mad speed, they evidently thought that we were anybody's game. Each and every one decided to take a shot at us.

For three miles we ran the gauntlet of firing from both sides of the road. I would see a soldier standing with his rifle at the ready waiting until we came opposite. Then "bang" he would let us have it. Sometimes they fired in squads; sometimes singly. The only reason why we were not riddled with bullets is because the Chinese soldier is the world's worst rifle shot. Most of them aimed directly at the car, when they aimed at all, and the bullets struck just behind us. Every now and then one would zip in close to my head but no one was hit. I really had the best of it because the others could not see what was going on and driving the car kept me busy. I expected every moment that one of the tires would be hit. A blowout at that speed would have turned us over.

Before long we could see the rearguard of the

retreating army and the sniping at us ceased. Still our troubles were far from being ended. The first retreating soldiers, three of them, asked for a ride. I thought that they might be a protection and let them stand on the running board of the car. Suddenly one of them saw an officer. Without a word he stepped backward off the car, rolled on the ground with his right hand under the rear wheel. As I put on the brakes it ground his hand and arm into the hard gravel road. I have never seen such a sight. His hand was simply shredded. I put on a tourniquet to stop the bleeding but he was only anxious for us to go.

A little further and we came to masses of infantry. Against my protests they piled on the car in such numbers that it could pull only in first speed. The inevitable happened when one fell off, breaking his leg. Things looked pretty bad. Three or four of the soldiers worked themselves into a rage, cocked their rifles and were just about to shoot us when an officer appeared.

Fortunately, he could speak Mandarin Chinese perfectly (the others talked a difficult Shantung dialect) and when I explained what had happened he cleared a passage so that we could drive off the

314

road into the fields. With much difficulty we got through the gates back to Peking.

I don't mind saying that we were all scared. It had been a nasty experience and taught us that the old order had changed very suddenly. No longer could we depend upon a foreign flag to protect us from the bullets of Chinese soldiers.

Until about three years ago there were certain well-understood matters of good form which must be observed in the conduct of war. For instance, it was unethical to start hostilities during the winter; as for fighting in the rain, it simply wasn't done. Chinese hate to get wet and one day I saw thousands of troops going up to the front each with an umbrella in a neat little sack on his back. Just behind them came the lantern brigade. Hundreds of men carrying kerosene lanterns on the ends of long poles!

There never are very many killed in a war even to-day. It becomes merely a matter of finances. Each side tries to outbuy the other. The one which has the most money, or can offer the greatest material advantages, wins. Often a General decides to play a lone hand and reap all the harvest.

As an instance, I remember Feng Yu-hsiang's *coup d' état* on October 23, 1924. While I was dressing in the morning my little son, George, ran into the room shouting, "There's a war. There's a war. No school today. I want to see the war."

I rang for the Boy, and asked him to explain. "No can tell," said he, "have got plenty soldiers. No can go outside house. Have got one policeman: he walk up and down. Soldiers no let him go out."

"Where is *tai-tai* (Mrs. Andrews)?"

"She go race course six o'clock. She no come back."

I was accustomed to Chinese but that did me in a bit I must confess. A war, my house surrounded by soldiers, George not able to go to school, my wife at the race course! The night before we had dined at the British Legation and danced until one o'clock in the morning. There wasn't any war up to that time nearer than the Shan-hai-kuan front three hundred miles away! Mrs. Andrews had planned to see the training of some of my race ponies and apparently she had gone.

One thing was certain, it was a devilish quiet war. I couldn't hear any shooting and a flock of pigeons with whistles on their tails circled peacefully above the house in the golden autumn sunlight.

There was no use getting excited so I had breakfast and my usual cigarette. Then I strolled out to the great gate of the compound to see what was happening. At least fifty Chinese were squatted on their heels in front of my door. The entrance to the *hutung* (street) was barricaded and on Morrison Street were lines of soldiers. I said to one of them in Chinese.

"Who is your General?"

"Feng Yu-hsiang."

"When did you come?"

"This morning at three o'clock."

"What are you going to do?"

"I don't know."

"What are your orders?"

"Not to let anyone go on the street."

And that was all I could get from him or from the others, so I tried the policeman. He was almost tearful because the soldiers wouldn't let him out of the *hutung* and he was losing much "face" with the crowd by suddenly being reduced to absolute impotence as an exponent of the law.

It was an extraordinary business. I knew my wife was well able to care for herself under most conditions, but with the city full of soldiers it seemed wise at least to try and discover where she was. But just as I was leaving the gate a car dashed up from the back entrance of the street scattering children, pigs and chickens in every direction. My wife jumped out, her face radiant.

"Oh, we've had such an amusing time," she cried. "When Colonel Smallwood and I started for the race course they wouldn't let us into Morrison Street so we slipped out the back way. The city is surrounded with soldiers—machine guns and artillery at the railway stations. They've taken over the telegraph and telephones and we're cut off. Isn't it fun?

"Feng Yu-hsiang has done it. He has deserted Wu Pei-fu and made a *coup d' état*. A rotten trick I call it."

"Did you see the ponies run?" I asked.

"Oh yes, of course. The soldiers stopped us at every gate and looked under the seat, but we went on to the race course. "Kara Nor" did a quarter in thirty flat. "Koko Nor" is dead lame but the "Pove" cantered a mile and finished the last quarter in thirty and one-fifth.

"They have arrested the President. Tsao is in his palace but I saw four soldiers with executioners' knives just outside. Do you think they will cut his head off? Has the baby's milk come? No! let's go after it. We'll bring the goat back with us in the car and keep it here. If there is going to be a war we've *got* to keep the goat here, that's all there is about it.

THE END OF THE JOURNEY.

A Village Feast in Mongolia.

Please may I have the goat here? You can put it in one of the stables and I'll learn to milk it!"

There was no use arguing the point. I had learned to save my breath when the subject was milk and the baby. But I did permit myself a heartfelt sigh while we went out to the stables to see which of my polo ponies would have to be ousted to make room for the goat.

It was awfully annoying to have a war drop on one "over night" so to speak. I had just returned from Mongolia where political affairs were in the normal state of disruption and was looking forward to a month of polo in Peking before packing the equipment for the next expedition.

While I was sadly contemplating the fact that the prospective goat would have to have the cleanest stall in the stables, my wife dashed off to see that the three *amahs* and the governess who constituted the baby's harem were properly "on the job." Five minutes later she had jammed my hat on my head, pushed me into the car, and we were off to learn "what was what" and to bring back the wretched goat.

My wife, having just come in, knew what streets were closed, so by keeping close to the old Imperial City wall, we avoided the main thoroughfares and came out near the entrance to the Legation Quarter. A dozen soldiers with red arm bands in the center of which were white tabs stopped us there but they only looked into the car and waved us on.

Half way to the Legation we overtook Major Wearne, Reuter's correspondent, and he gave us the news. Marshall Feng Yu-hsiang had deserted and left Wu Pei-fu "in the air" at Shan-hai-kuan. Feng had taken over Peking and issued a proclamation stating that since everyone was bored with the war, he and some of his generals had decided to stop it forthwith. He announced that there would be no disturbance and that the motto should be "business as usual." Peking was cut off from all communication except by wireless but there was no disorder, and the soldiers were behaving excellently. That was all that anyone knew at the moment.

With this information in hand my wife's thoughts again reverted to the goat, but by the time we reached the mission which supplies the milk for Peking's foreign babies I had marshalled my arguments, to wit: There was no immediate prospect of trouble: the goat was beautifully comfortable where it could gambol on the green and eat the grass in the mission compound: it would have no grass in my stables (although, of course, I would just love to have it there) and the change of food might seriously affect it's milk: if by any wild stretch of imagination there should be trouble I would risk life and limb to bring the goat into the American Legation with the baby and his *amahs*.

I could see that my wife was shaken and after she had two bottles of milk safely in her hands, she agreed that the goat might remain where it was for the present. Far be it from me to praise myself unduly but I must admit that I had a feeling of intense satisfaction which comes only when a delicate job has been well done. In fact I felt that I must go to the Club at once to discuss the matter with several of my men friends who likewise had small babies and wives who threatened them with goats. Of course, I didn't intend to be immodest about it, but I just wanted to see whether or not they had done as well as I had.

At the Club corks were popping madly and everyone was having a priceless time. Just why it was necessary to buy champagne no one could tell, but it was being bought all right and drunk, too. Feng had pulled off the cleverest *coup d' état* that had been staged in China for years. He was heartily denounced for having "double-crossed" Wu but it had been done so quietly and suddenly that we could not but admire that part of it.

There was no real information other than what I knew already but rumors were being manufactured every moment. I can't imagine what Peking would do without it's rumors; it simply lives on them. The Club is a sort of telephone switchboard and when its inmates return to the bosom of their families for tiffin or dinner news is radiated in every direction.

Many of the rumors found their way into print. Once Dr. Young of the Peking Union Medical College was bringing a number of mice to Peking for laboratory experiments and the cages had to be trans-shipped at Tientsin. Two newspapers published the following.

North China Star, Tientsin, October 18, 1924.

"Mice for the front—yes—for the front and not the circus. The very latest war cargo to pass Tientsin station yesterday for the front was a party of mice consisting of twenty cages each containing from fifty to sixty mice. They arrived here yesterday from Hsuchow and were immediately sent to the front. These mice were all carefully wrapped in soft cotton and fed with black beans. The use of

The Mongolian Lasso is a Long Light Birch Pole.

BREAKING THE WILD HORSES OF THE MONGOLIAN PLAINS.

these little animals remains a puzzle to many an eye-witness at the railway station."

Asiatic News Service, Peking *Leader*,

October 19, 1924.

"In addition to monkeys and bears, Marshall Wu Pei-fu has ordered about a hundred mice from Hsu-chow, Northern Kiangsu, and these little animals were packed in twenty cases for transportation to the Shan-hai-kuan front at once. It is reported that the Mukden troops are using poison gas and these rats will be employed for its detection at the battle fronts."

I remember at the time of the Japan earthquake it was impossible to learn what had become of several passenger ships which were in the harbor at Yokohama. The agent of the line was asked about the *Empress of Australia*. He was busy and didn't want to be bothered. "For all I know she may be in the center of Yokohama being used as a restaurant," he answered.

The next morning one of the local papers stated in headlines that "an unconfirmed report gives the *Empress of Australia* as having been cast by the tidal wave bodily into the city where she is being used by the authorities to house and feed the homeless."

Peking lives in a perpetual state of nerves. Political bombs explode every few days but if there happens to be an interlude something *must* be found to keep up the excitement.

A *coup d' état* such as Feng Yu-hsiang had just executed gave some perfectly delightful thrills. No one was really frightened for constant association with civil wars in China had shown us how "very civil" they were as one eminent Chinese remarked.

Pages were written about the political significance of this particular war but the real truth of the matter was that it had no deep significance whatsoever. It was merely a continuation of the personal rivalry of two generals, Chang Tso-lin and Wu Pei-fu. Both of them wanted to be the biggest frog in the pond and control China and it was inevitable that after the indecisive defeat which Wu had administered to Chang in 1922 that there should be another clash. Of course they had both issued patriotic notes about how their hearts bled for the poor people but no one noticed that they stopped making the poor people bleed for **them**!

CHAPTER XIX

I RETURNED to the American Museum of Natural History after two years of wandering in the Far East. The first man I met in the foyer was Carl Akeley of African fame. We hugged each other, for there were few men who inspired such deep affection among his friends as "old Ake."

"What's up, Ake. Are you going or coming or staying?"

"I'm just leaving, Roy. In a week we sail for British East. The African Hall is a real going concern. It has been a long fight, but at last it is over the top. Come up to my room."

I went. In the half light of a partitioned hall an elephant bulked hugely almost to the ceiling. Two life-sized models of Masai warriors poised with spear and shield against a pair of charging lions. A white rhinoceros stood in majestic repose beside the window. The floor was strewn with a mass of half packed equipment, boxes and débris. An elephant gun lay upon the desk.

We picked our way through the litter and sat

down. Puffing away at his brown pipe, Ake told me of his efforts in the last two years to obtain financial support for his greatest life-work, the African Hall.

"I have five men, each of whom have made themselves financially responsible for a mammal group," said he. "Mr. George Eastman and Dan Pomeroy are going to Africa with me for the beginning."

Then we looked at the model of the hall which Akeley had constructed years ago when he first conceived the plan. Everything in miniature, to scale; the groups, murals, floor models, just as the hall would appear in its completed form. In spite of his infectious enthusiasm Akeley looked like a broken man, physically. Long ago in Africa he had been attacked by a wounded leopard. It was in the half-dusk of a summer's evening. He was returning to camp after a fruitless search for a wart hog, when he saw a yellow streak flash across a sandy river bottom. As he fired he realized that it was a foolish thing to do. The bullet broke the leopard's foot. Akeley's rifle jammed and he turned to run. The beast landed on his back, tearing at his left arm above the elbow. Akeley twisted about to keep his stomach away from the claws which were ripping his legs like white hot irons and with his right hand gripped the leopard's throat. They rolled in the sand together, Akeley on top. With his knees pressing into the beast and breaking ribs, he strangled the leopard with his bare hands. Akeley was a mass of dripping blood and mangled flesh when he staggered into camp where D. G. Elliot was awaiting him for dinner.

Years later a bull elephant had crushed his chest. He never forgot that night of agony in the African jungle, helpless, listening to the roars of lions and the yelps of prowling hyenas, expecting every moment that they would catch his man-scent on the wind.

Again he lay almost dead of the terrible blackwater fever at a remote mission station. Cables from the Museum imploring him to leave Africa and save his life were disregarded. Until his job was done he would not go.

Years of inspired work in the nerve racking life of New York had produced superb achievement in art, invention and natural history. He stood a unique figure, yet unspoiled, enthusiastic as a boy, ready to start again on the last Great Exploration from which he never returned.

His whole life was an example of the modern museum ideal, objective education. He had a pas-

sion for perfection. Always was he struggling to
find new and better ways to bring a selected section
of some far country to the people of America; to
reproduce that scene in the Museum so perfectly that
they might see what he saw and know what he
knew; to have every natural fact accurate that the
lesson it taught might be a true lesson.

We often talked of the difficulties of financing our
respective work and of the obligations we incurred
to those who made it possible. I remember that he
said one day: "Roy, sometime before I die I'm going on my own. I'll build my little camp-fire in
Africa and I'll sit there and smoke my pipe and do
nothing and be happy because I won't have to make
good to anybody."

"Yes," said I, "you will *not*. You know darned
well you'll have to make good to yourself. When
you kill an elephant, why do you slave in the heat
and flies and fever to save its skin? Do you think
it is because of the people who gave their dollars to
send you to the jungle? Rot. Why do you go there
anyway? You know well enough you can't help but
do it. You were born that way."

Ake looked at me and grinned. "I suppose you
are right. I guess I'm cursed with a museum complex."

TEMPLE COURTYARD NEAR PEKING.

MR. AKELEY AT WORK ON AN ELEPHANT MODEL.

"Not cursed, Ake; blessed, you mean. We are all like that or we wouldn't be here. It's the only way we can be happy. Whether we spend our own money or somebody else's doesn't make a bit of difference. We gave ourselves the job and it is ourselves we have to satisfy."

Those of us who saw Ake make a group knew how right I was. The animals had to be perfect specimens of their kind or he never pulled a trigger. The notes and photographs he made, the drawings of difficult anatomical parts, the plaster casts and models were all an effort for perfect reproduction. The chemical treatment of the skin and its subsequent mounting meant weeks of work and constant experimentation with new methods. Every flower and bush and leaf, even the dirt itself, must come from the very spot he had selected to reproduce. He didn't have to do all that to fool the public. A handful of gravel from a New York pit might look as well as that from an African desert. But Akeley wasn't trying to fool the public. He didn't want to just "get by." He was striving to tell a true story because he stood for the modern museum spirit.

His ideal for the African Hall was to bring Africa to New York. In his great plan he had selected typical animals of various parts of the country. Each group was to teach a lesson in the general natural history of that particular region; its animal and bird life, geography, botany and their human relationships. Every detail had been carefully considered years ago. It took him six months to make the scale model of the hall.

Akeley is dead. His body lies peacefully in its last sleep on the slopes of a beautiful mountain in the Belgian Congo, but his spirit lives in the African Hall and in the whole Museum. The work goes on in the hands of his devoted students, as he had planned.

Except for a dinner together at the Century Club the first meeting with Akeley after my return from two years in Mongolia was the last. He sailed the next week. I left his studio that morning to greet Dr. George H. Sherwood, Director of the Museum. Then went to the north wing to see Dr. Frank M. Chapman, Curator of Birds. Twenty years ago I had served him and Dr. J. A. Allen as general assistant, not long after I had graduated from floorwashing in the Museum. Chapman was preparing for flight to his beloved Southland. On an island in Panama, overlooking the Canal, he had established a research station. There he spends the winters studying the habits of birds, writing and obtaining data for new groups in his magnificent halls.

Frank Chapman typifies the modern museum as truly as did Akeley. He is a great teacher; without a doubt the greatest living teacher of ornithology. His books have shown hundreds of thousands how to know and love birds. His scientific writings have won him medals and honor over all the world. His bird groups in the American Museum are each one a complete lesson in natural science. I remember what a sensation the great flamingo group created the first year I came to the Museum. No one knew how these beautiful birds nested. Chapman discovered a colony of them in the Bahama Islands. He went there with the late Louis Agassiz Fuertes, the famous bird artist and erected a "blind" right in the middle of the nesting site on a mud flat. Day after day he and Fuertes watched and photographed the birds, some of them within a few feet of the camera. They collected specimens for the group and a dozen of the mud nests, raised like an overturned pail, to keep the eggs above water. Fuertes painted the background and made portrait studies of the birds. The completed group told all that there was to know about the life story of these strange birds.

Year after year Chapman explored the jungles of

South and Central America, bringing enormous collections to the Museum for scientific study. He described hundreds of new and strange species, elucidating their life histories and faunal and geographic relationships.

Across the hall from Chapman's room sat Harold Anthony, Curator of Mammals, in my old office. He was surrounded by maps of South America. In a few weeks he, too, would be off to the jungles to do the same thing for mammals that all his life Chapman had been doing with birds.

So I found it in every department of the Museum. My colleagues were either going to, or coming from, the far places of the earth. Thirty-five expeditions were in the field that year; at times there have been as many as sixty. The constant stream of new collections, new facts and data, flowing into the institution make its life blood. They keep the Museum a living, vital force in the educational life not only of the city and nation but of the entire world.

Behind it all shaping the policies and ultimate destiny of the Museum stand the President and Board of Trustees. Men of large affairs in the world of finance, they give their time and money that the facts of nature may be made plain for all to read.

338

President Henry Fairfield Osborn, himself a scientist of international distinction, has devoted his entire life and much of his private fortune to the cause of science. The growth of the Museum is largely in his hands. New buildings, negotiations with the city and state, international affiliations and problems of finance take far too much of the time which should be left free for his scientific research.

In the hands of Director George H. Sherwood lies the administration of the Museum. Only a man of broad scientific knowledge, of infinite patience, tact and general business ability could fill the director's chair. He is the executive officer of the Museum ship, the one who must see that all the departments of the Museum function smoothly and in harmony. He pulls the wires that make the wheels go around. He settles personal difficulties, gets us out of trouble, and handles so many details that a full chronicle of one week's activities would fill a dozen chapters of a book.

An institution which spends more than a million and a half dollars yearly is in the class of big business. The financial departments alone are not unlike those of a great department store. Dinosaur bones, snakes, fishes, birds and mammals are our stock, but accounting for the money and the materials that are handled is much the same.

It is even more difficult than that of a store because the Museum is a joint institution. The City of New York owns the land and building and gives us $452,374.00 a year for maintenance; the collections and the endowment of $12,162,549.00 are the property of the incorporated Board of Trustees. Up to the present the building has cost $8,390,599.00, but it is less than half completed; the estimated cost of the projected Museum is $24,394,343.00.

The administrators who control the destinies of New York City are an intelligent group; nay more, they might even be called hard-boiled business men. Such vast expenditures would not be encouraged unless the city and the nation were receiving something of value for every dollar. That something is objective education which they realize can be better supplied by a great modern Museum than by any other means.

In 1927, ten million school children of New York and neighboring cities were reached by the Museum activities; nearly two and one-half million people actually visited the Museum. Every day autos leave the Museum carrying "loan collections" of birds, mammals, minerals, etc., to various schools of the city. These remain for a short time and then are replaced by others. In 1927, more than a million and a half children studied these collections. Classes and whole schools make periodical excursions to the Museum to see exhibits which illustrate some particular course of study. Hundreds of thousands of lantern slides and motion picture films are loaned to public schools. A teacher need only apply to the Curator of Public Education to arrange an illustrated lecture on almost any subject of natural science either in the Museum or at the school itself. There are collections and study rooms especially arranged for the blind.

In 1926 a special school Service Building was completed by the City at a cost of $883,800.00. As Professor Osborn said, "The chief purpose of this beautiful building is to interpret and extend knowledge of the work of all departments of this great Museum to the youth of our schools. There is a kind of liaison between the American Museum and our colossal School System."

The public reads much of the expeditions which return from the Arctic or the desert or tropic jungles. The reports state that so many thousand animals and birds or so many cases of fossil bones have been obtained. But few people see or know what becomes of these vast collections after they have reached the Museum and before they are placed on exhibition. There is romance and excitement there just as in gathering the specimens in the field.

As an example, consider the story of the dinosaur eggs. We were working in a great deposit of dinosaur bones at a place called the Flaming Cliffs in the very center of the Gobi Desert. One day, George Olsen, one of our collectors, came into camp and remarked that he had found some strange fossil eggs. We rather laughed about it, for we thought his "eggs" would prove to be sandstone concretions. Still we were interested enough to go with him to see for ourselves. Very soon we realized that we were looking at the first dinosaur eggs that ever had been seen by human eyes. Three had broken out of a sandstone ledge which was rapidly disintegrating. Bits of shell still remained in the rock; it was probable that the ledge contained more eggs.

We had neither the time nor instruments to obtain them if they were there. Finally, Walter Granger, Chief Palæontologist, decided to send a large section of the ledge to the Museum. It is a difficult job to transport a rock weighing hundreds of pounds from the center of the Gobi Desert to New York, and it would have been rather a joke on us if there had been nothing in it—a pretty expensive joke, too! But the rock was sent and it reached the Museum safely. Then began the interesting job of unwrapping a package ninety-five million years old! No one knew what we would find, or even if it would contain anything at all. The preparators started operations on the upper part of the block. Working with tiny steel chisels and scrapers, they struck bone almost immediately. To our amazement they soon exposed the skeleton of a small dinosaur lying just beneath the surface. It was a little fellow only four feet long and toothless, a new type to science. Professor Osborn is convinced that it fed upon the eggs of other dinosaurs; that it was an egg thief. Probably it was in the act of digging into this nest when it was smothered by a violent sandstorm and buried with the eggs that it had come to rob. When the skeleton had been removed there was still two-thirds of the block untouched. Would there be anything else in it? Bit by bit the preparators worked away the stone. In the very center of the slab were thirteen almost perfect eggs lying in a double circle. They lay just as they had been left ninety-five millions of years ago by the old dinosaur when she covered them for the last time and went away, never to return. But the preparation was not accomplished in a few hours or days. It required weeks of careful work to pick the rock away bit by bit and expose the eggs.

The skull of the giant *Baluchitherium*, the largest mammal that ever lived upon the earth, gives another story. By chance the jaw and other bones had been discovered one evening in a badland draw a thousand miles out in the Gobi Desert. Granger thought that he had obtained all that remained of the specimen, but the next morning I returned to the spot with Shackelford, our photographer. In the bottom of another ravine I saw the huge skull partly buried in the sand. It had broken out of the hillside as the rock was worn away by the action of weathering and rolled to the bottom of the slope. For four days Granger worked with two men to bandage and remove the skull. Meanwhile others of us searched the surrounding slopes and ravines for broken parts. Some were found three or four hundred yards away, where they had been carried by running water. It was a difficult task to box the skull there in the desert with only boards from gasoline cases for material. Then it journeyed a thousand miles across the desert on the backs of camels through the blizzards of early winter. At Kalgan we put it on a train for Peking, where it was care-

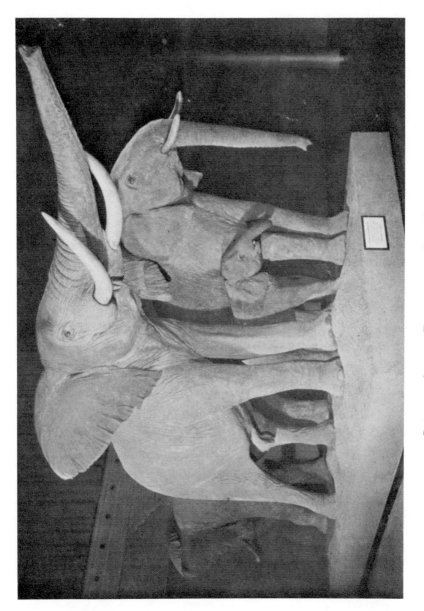

GROUP OF AFRICAN ELEPHANTS BY CARL AKELEY.

HABITAT GROUP OF AMERICAN EGRETS: DR. FRANK M. CHAPMAN.

fully repacked. Then it went to Tientsin, across the Pacific, and on to New York. Twelve thousand miles the skull travelled before it reached the Museum. Almost immediately preparators began work on its reconstruction. There were six hundred and forty-two pieces, some of them only tiny fragments. No one knew what the animal looked like because this was the first skull of the species to be discovered.

With infinite care, Otto Falkenbach, one of the Museum's expert preparators, worked day after day piecing together the hundreds of broken bits and restoring the missing parts. Every morning Professor Osborn and Dr. W. D. Matthew discussed the reconstruction, using all their knowledge of related groups to properly place the bones. Six months had passed before the work was completed and the restored skull was ready for exhibition. Six months of labor and constant study. The public knew nothing of that. To them the skull had been received at the Museum from Mongolia; they read that much in the newspapers. The next time they visited the Museum there it was on exhibition.

I remember that some years ago when a shark group was being prepared in the fish hall, there was a good deal of discussion about what the color of the water would be at a certain depth. Some of us thought that it should be greenish-yellow and others were certain that it must be bluish-green. Finally the artist got himself into a diving suit and with special paints sat on a rock fifteen or twenty feet under water and settled the question beyond argument with the picture which he made.

I don't suppose that many people would select the anatomy of the malarial mosquito as a particularly interesting subject for two years' study. Personally, I'm all against mosquitoes and I'm certain that about two hours' inspection of his insides would suffice me for life. But that is just because I don't happen to have an insect complex. Luckily there are others who do. I say "luckily" because those men produced the models of the malarial mosquito, enlarged seventy-five diameters, in the American Museum of Natural History. Even with my firm prejudice against mosquitoes I can stand fascinated in front of those cases learning just how he breeds and lives and does his stuff. Aside from their scientific value, they are marvels of work in glass and wax. Herman Mueller, the glass blower, is responsible for truly wonderful enlargements of insects and invertebrates which open a page in the book of life that otherwise would remain closed to millions of Museum visitors.

The Department of Preparation is always more interesting to me than any other. Perhaps it is because I started my career in the Museum by washing its floors; perhaps because of the particular kind of work it does. The miniature scale models of new halls are made there. Long before the city appropriates the money for another section of the Museum building, details of the exhibition halls and laboratories are in preparation. Models are constructed and every group installed to scale. Then in larger replicas of each exhibit the posing of the figures is studied and miniature backgrounds are painted. It is so carefully worked out that when the actual group is to be prepared the task is merely to copy the model.

Mounting of the large animals for a group is no longer a simple matter. Carl Akeley did more than any other man to advance taxidermy to a high art. A modern museum taxidermist never can be more than passable unless he possesses considerable skill as a sculptor. That was one of Akeley's greatest gifts. His bronzes of elephants, lions, gorillas and human figures are given first rank among world sculptors. The "Wounded Comrade" is perhaps his best known bronze. It shows two huge elephants half carrying between them an injured companion who can just maintain his feet. These beautiful statuettes grew out of studies for animals he was about to mount. After he had worked out every detail of the anatomy in the miniature model of the beast, it was enlarged to life size. Over the plaster cast made of the clay figure the skin was laid. Akeley used to work months on a single specimen. When the animal was done it all but breathed. His students, under the direction of James L. Clark, follow in the footsteps of their master.

Years ago Akeley developed a commercial invention of considerable importance as the direct result of his first attempt to mount an elephant. He was then in the Field Museum of Natural History, Chicago. The greatest problem was to obtain a light body for the huge beast. Eventually he conceived the idea of placing the prepared skin over a framework and coating the inside with soft cement which could be modeled before it dried. But how was he to lay on the cement? To spray it would be the most satisfactory method, but there was no cement spray on the market. Ake invented one.

The elephant was mounted, satisfactorily for that time, and Akeley found himself in possession of a cement gun. The Field Museum, which then was housed in one of the old World's Fair buildings, needed repairs on the outside walls. Akeley made them with the cement gun. This demonstrated its commercial importance so effectually that a company was formed to put it on the market. The cement gun was used successfully in construction work of the Panama Canal and in making the cement ships developed during the world war.

The Akeley Camera was a direct outcome of his attempts to photograph wild animals in Africa. No satisfactory camera existed, so Ake invented one which is indispensable to the nature photographer. Akeley's contributions to Museum technique are so fundamental that no one can write about modern museum exhibition without making it almost a story of his achievements. To those of us who knew and loved this great man there can be no higher satisfaction than to "Render unto Cæsar what is Cæsar's."

The Museum has of course hundreds of thousands of what are called "study specimens," viz., objects not of exhibition value but necessary for scientific study and delineation of a group or species or the facts of evolution. There are several hundred thousand birds, and probably half as many mammals all properly catalogued and indexed in those collections.

I would not venture to say how many insects. Their proper care entails much work and expense.

The collections come from almost every country of the world. Foreign investigators are always welcome and hardly a week passes that some scientist from abroad is not installed in an office with whatever specimens he wishes to study open to his research.

Many of the exhibits are world famous. After the war when Clemenceau visited America he insisted on being driven immediately to the American Museum to see the giant carnivorous dinosaur, *Tyrannosaurus.* For years this amazing beast had had a peculiar fascination for the venerable "Tiger" of France. Few visitors to New York miss the dinosaur eggs. The evolution of the horse, from the tiny four-toed Eocene type, no larger than a small dog, up to the thoroughbred of today, is known from Vladivostock to Valparaiso. Dozens of other exhibits are unique and equally famous.

I remember the first day I visited the Museum as a supplicant for a job. I arrived too early in the morning and walked twice around the vast pile of buildings. Then I sat down on a rock just inside the entrance to the Park at Eighty-first Street. I looked at the Museum and wondered what kind of a place it was; what sort of men I should meet there. Would it be filled with lines of dusty cases in cobwebby halls? Would the curators be little stoop-shouldered men wearing spectacles and long beards who would peer at me as though I were a strange and rather unwelcome insect? That was what the "funny papers" had led me to expect. I was fresh from a small mid-western town and had never seen a great museum. Although Osborn, Chapman, Lucas and others were my youthful gods, I had little conception of their personalities.

What a shock I got when I stepped into the vast marble foyer of the Museum and saw it as it is! Could anything be more unlike my preconceived ideas than the curators themselves? Instead of little bespectacled scientists wearing black alpaca coats, I found alert, well dressed men who would not look out of place in a banker's chair. All of it was different and bewildering.

But at that, my first conception of a museum curator was not unlike the popular idea even today. A thousand times at least people have remarked to me:

"You don't look like a scientist." Because I wear clean linen, patronize a barber and a decent tailor,

353

like dancing, polo and everything to do with a horse, they are rather disappointed. How many times my dinner partner has said: "I wondered what I could talk to you about. I thought I'd never be able to understand anything you said."

But I think the modern museum is fast dispelling the idea that its curators must be the type of men who live in the clouds of their own great intellects and forget their neckties when they dine out. Natural science has been humanized. To make it plain for all to read is the job of those of us who "heroically" dedicate our lives to a museum because we couldn't be happy doing anything else.

The best museum men and the best explorers are born, not made. It must be in the blood, it cannot be acquired. A man without an intense desire to do that particular kind of thing can never be more than a moderate success at most. The life is not all pleasure and excitement. The adventure and romance are so attractive that dozens of boys want to try their hands at the game, but few last very long. There is too much work, which becomes mere drudgery if one's heart is not in it. There is the certain knowledge that one must relinquish all hope of gaining worldly goods. There will be a living, but that is all if one is not endowed with exceptional gifts. Still it gives a kind of happiness that money can never buy.

I used to dream of the days when I could lead my own expeditions and plan my own exhibition halls. Those dreams have come true and unlike so many dreams the realization is greater than the anticipation.